POCKET
POSTERS

GCSE **Maths**
Revision Guide
Higher

Improving understanding through colour and clarity

Get your FREE digital book!

This book includes a free digital edition for use on a PC, Mac, tablet or smartphone.

Go to ddedu.co.uk/maths-higher
and enter this code...

Code: MAHULA42

Ratio and Proportion

Geometry and Measures

Probability and Statistics

Maths Jargon

+	Addition	4 **+** 3 = 7
−	Subtraction	7 **−** 5 = 2
✕	Multiplication	2 **✕** 4 = 8
÷	Division	12 **÷** 3 = 4
=	Is equal to	$\frac{1}{2}$ **=** 0.5
≠	Is not equal to	3 **≠** 4
≈	Approximate	a **≈** 4,000

Integers

0	120	5	−73	−394	88

Integers are whole numbers, including zero and negative numbers.

Rational & Irrational Numbers

Rational numbers are numbers that can be written as fractions, including integers, fractions and decimals. These numbers are either terminating or recurring decimals.

$$3 = \frac{3}{1} \qquad \frac{1}{7} \qquad 0.\dot{3} = \frac{1}{3} \qquad 0.25 = \frac{1}{4}$$

Irrational numbers are numbers that cannot be written as fractions. When represented as a decimal number, they do not terminate or repeat.

π	$\sqrt{8}$	$-\sqrt{11}$

Multiples

Every number has **multiples**. For example, every number that 3 goes into is a **multiple** of 3, so **3, 6, 9, 12, 15, 18**... etc. are all multiples of 3.

The **lowest common multiple (LCM)** of two numbers is the smallest whole number which is a multiple of both numbers.

The LCM of 4 and 10 is 20:

Multiples of 4: 4, 8, 12, 16, **20**, 24

Multiples of 10: 10, **20**, 30, 40, 50

Factors

Every number has **factors**. The **factors** of **12** are **1, 2, 3, 4, 6** and **12** because all of these numbers go exactly into 12.

The **highest common factor (HCF)** of two numbers is the largest whole number which is a factor of both numbers.

The HCF of 18 and 30 is 6:

Factors of 18: 1, 2, 3, **6**, 9, 18

Factors of 30: 1, 2, 3, 5, **6**, 10, 15, 30

Squares & Cubes

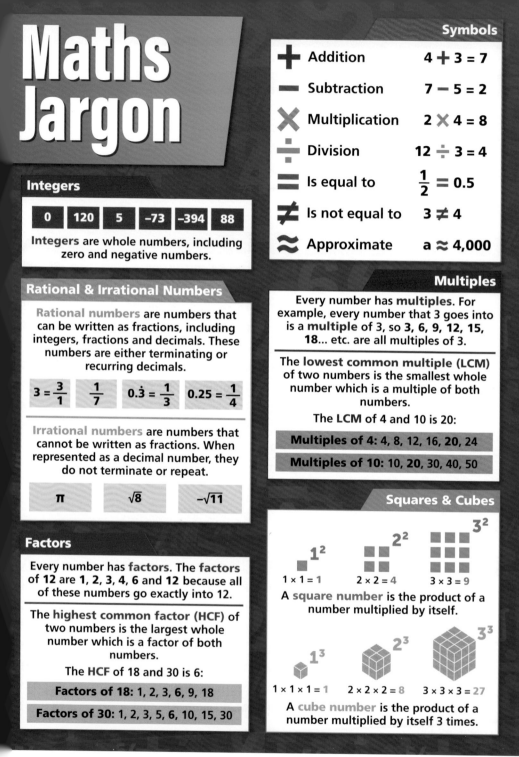

$1²$ $2²$ $3²$

1 × 1 = 1   2 × 2 = 4   3 × 3 = 9

A **square number** is the product of a number multiplied by itself.

$1³$ $2³$ $3³$

1 × 1 × 1 = 1   2 × 2 × 2 = 8   3 × 3 × 3 = 27

A **cube number** is the product of a number multiplied by itself 3 times.

daydream
EDUCATION

Approximate

Not exact; close to the exact value. This often means rounding to a significant figure or decimal point.

Pi is approximately equal to 3.14. $\pi \approx 3.14$.

Convert

To change from one unit of measure to another.

If £1 = \$0.9 convert £20 into dollars.

Calculate

To find the answer to a mathematical problem.

Calculate the cost of 10 apples when 1 apple costs 50p.

Estimate

To calculate an approximate value for a number. Usually, rounding each number within a calculation to a significant figure will make it easier.

$$\frac{31 \times 9.98}{0.46} \approx \frac{30 \times 10}{0.5} \approx \frac{300}{0.5} \approx 600$$

Evaluate

To work out the value of a numerical or algebraic expression.

Evaluate $x^2 + 1$ when $x = 2$.

Express

To represent or show something in a different form or way.

15 out of 30 pupils passed their maths exam.
Express this as a percentage.

Identify

To find, determine or establish the answer to something.

Identify how many sides and angles a square has.

Simplify

To make simpler. In maths, this can involve reducing a fraction to its simplest form or collecting algebraic expressions together.

$$3x + 5 + 2x - 4 \implies 5x + 1$$

Construct

To draw geometric shapes and angles.

Construct a right angle triangle using a compass and a rule.

Prove

To demonstrate, with evidence, that something is true. A question may ask you to prove algebraically.

Prove that angles in the same segment and standing on the same chord are always equal.

Place Value

The value of each digit in a number depends upon its position or place. The position, or place, of each digit represents a power of ten.

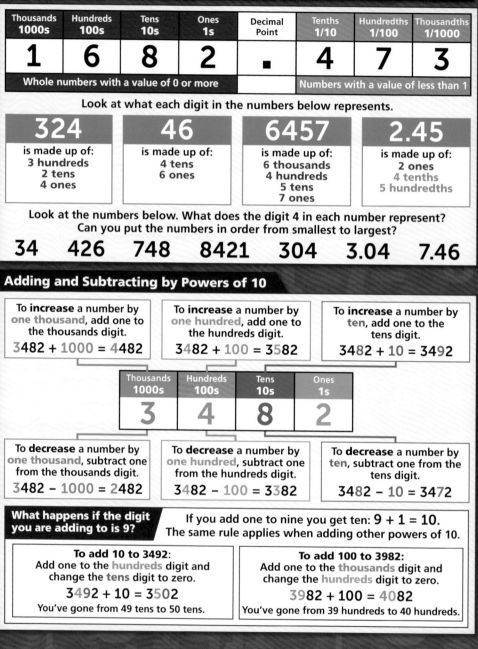

Thousands 1000s	Hundreds 100s	Tens 10s	Ones 1s	Decimal Point	Tenths 1/10	Hundredths 1/100	Thousandths 1/1000
1	6	8	2	.	4	7	3

Whole numbers with a value of 0 or more — Numbers with a value of less than 1

Look at what each digit in the numbers below represents.

324
is made up of:
3 hundreds
2 tens
4 ones

46
is made up of:
4 tens
6 ones

6457
is made up of:
6 thousands
4 hundreds
5 tens
7 ones

2.45
is made up of:
2 ones
4 tenths
5 hundredths

Look at the numbers below. What does the digit 4 in each number represent? Can you put the numbers in order from smallest to largest?

34   426   748   8421   304   3.04   7.46

Adding and Subtracting by Powers of 10

To **increase** a number by one thousand, add one to the thousands digit.
3482 + 1000 = 4482

To **increase** a number by one hundred, add one to the hundreds digit.
3482 + 100 = 3582

To **increase** a number by ten, add one to the tens digit.
3482 + 10 = 3492

Thousands 1000s	Hundreds 100s	Tens 10s	Ones 1s
3	4	8	2

To **decrease** a number by one thousand, subtract one from the thousands digit.
3482 – 1000 = 2482

To **decrease** a number by one hundred, subtract one from the hundreds digit.
3482 – 100 = 3382

To **decrease** a number by ten, subtract one from the tens digit.
3482 – 10 = 3472

What happens if the digit you are adding to is 9?

If you add one to nine you get ten: 9 + 1 = 10. The same rule applies when adding other powers of 10.

To add 10 to 3492:
Add one to the hundreds digit and change the tens digit to zero.
3492 + 10 = 3502
You've gone from 49 tens to 50 tens.

To add 100 to 3982:
Add one to the thousands digit and change the hundreds digit to zero.
3982 + 100 = 4082
You've gone from 39 hundreds to 40 hundreds.

8

daydream EDUCATION

Prime Numbers

A **prime number** is a whole number that has only **two factors:** itself and 1.

For example, **7** is a **prime number** because it has only **two factors: 7** and **1.**

$$7 \div 7 = 1$$ and $$7 \div 1 = 7$$

2 is the lowest and only even prime number.

Any number can be written as a **product of prime factors** - a string of prime numbers that when multiplied together, total the original number.

Factor Trees

A factor tree is used to find the prime factor decomposition of a number.

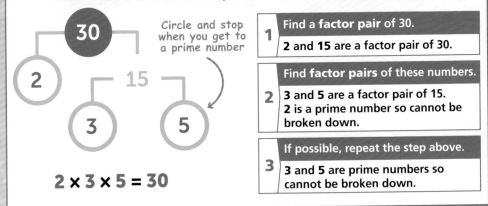

Circle and stop when you get to a prime number

$$2 \times 3 \times 5 = 30$$

1 | Find a **factor pair** of 30.
2 and 15 are a factor pair of 30.

2 | Find **factor pairs** of these numbers.
3 and 5 are a factor pair of 15.
2 is a prime number so cannot be broken down.

3 | If possible, repeat the step above.
3 and 5 are prime numbers so cannot be broken down.

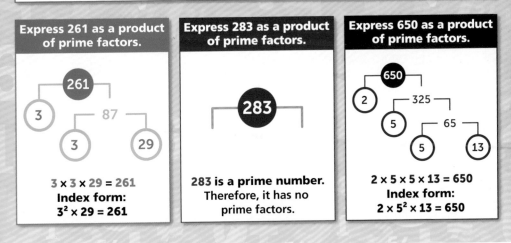

Express 261 as a product of prime factors.

$$3 \times 3 \times 29 = 261$$
Index form:
$$3^2 \times 29 = 261$$

Express 283 as a product of prime factors.

283 is a prime number.
Therefore, it has no prime factors.

Express 650 as a product of prime factors.

$$2 \times 5 \times 5 \times 13 = 650$$
Index form:
$$2 \times 5^2 \times 13 = 650$$

Order of Operations

When calculations involve multiple operations, they must be performed in a specific order.

The acronym **BIDMAS** is used to remember the correct order of operation.

B Brackets	**Brackets** first	$(6 + 2)$
I Indices	Then **indices** or roots	3^2
D Division	Then **divide** or **multiply** in order from left to right	$\dfrac{2 \times 4}{3}$
M Multiplication		
A Addition	Finally, **add** or **subtract** in order from left to right	$3 + 6 - 2$
S Subtraction		

$4 + 2 \times 3$

$2 \times 3 = 6$
$4 + 6 = 10$

B ▶ none
I ▶ none
D or M ▶ $2 \times 3 = 6$
A or S ▶ $4 + 6 = 10$

$20 \div (3 + 2)$

$3 + 2 = 5$
$20 \div 5 = 4$

B ▶ $3 + 2 = 5$
I ▶ none
D or M ▶ $20 \div 5 = 4$
A or S ▶ none

$5 + 3^2 - 6 \times 4$

$3^2 = 9$
$6 \times 4 = 24$
$5 + 9 = 14$
$14 - 24 = -10$

B ▶ none
I ▶ $3^2 = 9$
D or M ▶ $6 \times 4 = 24$
A or S ▶ $5 + 9 = 14$
    $14 - 24 = -10$

$6 - 2 + 4 - 3$

$6 - 2 = 4$
$4 + 4 = 8$
$8 - 3 = 5$

B ▶ none
I ▶ none
D or M ▶ none
A or S ▶ $6 - 2 = 4$
    $4 + 4 = 8$
    $8 - 3 = 5$

$(2^2 + 4)^2 \times 4$

$2^2 = 4$
$4 + 4 = 8$
$8^2 = 64$
$64 \times 4 = 256$

B ▶ $2^2 = 4$
    $4 + 4 = 8$
I ▶ $8^2 = 64$
D or M ▶ $64 \times 4 = 256$
A or S ▶ none

Within brackets, order of operations still apply so indices are performed before addition.

$(3 + 8 \div 2)^2$

$8 \div 2 = 4$
$3 + 4 = 7$
$7^2 = 49$

B ▶ $8 \div 2 = 4$
    $3 + 4 = 7$
I ▶ $7^2 = 49$
D or M ▶ none
A or S ▶ none

Within brackets, order of operations still apply so division is performed before addition.

daydream EDUCATION

Estimating

Sometimes you need to estimate answers to questions. This is often achieved by rounding the numbers in a question to one or two significant figures (s.f.) so that you can perform the calculation in your head.

Estimate the answer to $\frac{(692 + 22)}{(32 \times 1.8)}$.

1 Round all numbers to 1 s.f.

$$\frac{692 + 22}{32 \times 1.8} = \frac{(700 + 20)}{(30 \times 2)}$$

2 Perform the calculations.

$$\frac{(700 + 20)}{(30 \times 2)} = \frac{720}{60} = 12$$

A circle has a radius of 5 cm. Estimate the area of the circle.

1 Round all numbers to 1 or 2 s.f.

Area $= \pi r^2$
Area $= 3 \times 5^2$ ← π has been rounded to 3.

2 Perform the calculations.

3×5^2
$3 \times 25 = 75$ cm

Estimate the value of $\sqrt{70}$.

1 Find the square numbers that are either side of 70.

Square numbers:
36 49 64 81 100

2 Work out which square number 70 is closer to, and use this to estimate the decimal digit.

$64 = 8 \times 8$ $81 = 9 \times 9$
70 is slightly closer to 64 so a good estimate for the answer is 8.4.

Bounds

When a number is rounded to a specified degree of accuracy, the exact value could be anything from **half a unit below** to **half a unit above** the rounded number.

Rounded to the nearest 0.1 kg, Matthew's weight (*w*) is 76.4 kg.

lower bound — upper bound

76.30   76.35   76.40   76.45   76.50

The interval for Matthew's exact weight can be written as:
$76.35 \leq w < 76.45$

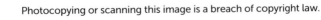

daydream
EDUCATION

Rounding Numbers

use exact numbers, so rounding is used to provide simpler numbers that are easier to use.

Rounding Using a Number Line

Number lines are used to help determine whether to round a number up or down.

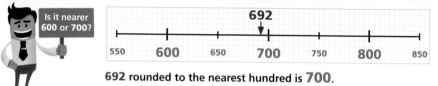

Is it nearer 600 or 700?

692

| 550 | **600** | 650 | **700** | 750 | **800** | 850 |

692 rounded to the nearest hundred is **700**.
The number line shows that **692** is closer to **700** than it is to **600**.

To round **2743** to the nearest ten, you need to identify whether it is nearer 2740 or 2750.

2743

| 2725 | **2730** | 2735 | **2740** | 2745 | **2750** | 2755 |

Is it nearer 2740 or 2750?

2743 rounded to the nearest ten is **2740**.
The number line shows that **2743** is closer to **2740** than it is to **2750**.

The same rule applies when rounding to decimal places.

Is it nearer 2.7 or 2.8?

2.72

| 2.55 | **2.6** | 2.65 | **2.7** | 2.75 | **2.8** | 2.85 |

2.72 rounded to one decimal place is **2.7**.
The number line shows that **2.72** is closer to **2.7** than it is to **2.8**.
When rounding numbers to decimal places, only consider the digits **after** the decimal point.

Rounding Without a Number Line

Without a number line, look at the **first digit to the right of the digit you are rounding**.

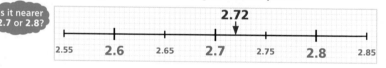

If the number is **less than 5**, leave it alone.	**1734** rounded to the nearest hundred is **1700**. — *less than 5 – leave it alone* **53.41** rounded to the nearest whole number is **53**. — *less than 5 – leave it alone*
If the number is **5 or more**, round up.	**77** rounded to the nearest ten is **80**. — *5 or more – round up* **3.14159** rounded to three decimal places is **3.142**. — *5 or more – round up*

Don't forget to put in the zeros.

daydream
EDUCATION

Significant Figures

If something is 'significant' it is large or important.
Therefore, 'most significant' means 'largest' or 'most important'.

	Hundreds	Tens	Ones		Tenths
In the number, 169.2, the most significant figure is **1** because it has the largest value, 100.	**1**	**6**	**9**	**•**	**2**

The first significant figure in a number, is the first digit that is not 0. Any leading zeros are insignificant (placeholders).	0302.14	00.507	0.00621

Rounding to Significant Figures

To round to significant figures, identify the significant figure that is being rounded to and round as normal.

To round 34562 to 1 significant figure:	**1**	Identify the first significant figure.	**34562**
	2	Look at the digit to the right of the one that is being rounded to. It is less than 5 so leave it alone.	**34562**
	3	Replace all digits after the first significant figure with zeros.	**30000**

34562 rounded to 1 significant figure is 30000.

To round 7.894 to 2 significant figures:	**1**	Identify the second significant figure.	**7.894**
	2	Look at the digit to the right of the one that is being rounded to. It is 5 or more so round up.	**7.894 → 7.9**
	3	When rounding decimals, there is no need to add zeros after the significant figures.	**7.9**

7.894 rounded to 2 significant figures is 7.9.

To round 0.0465279 to 3 significant figures:	**1**	Identify the third significant figure.	**0.0465279**
	2	Look at the digit to the right of the one that is being rounded to. It is less than 5 so leave it alone.	**0.0465279**
	3	When rounding decimals, there is no need to add zeros after the significant figures.	**0.0465**

0.0465279 rounded to 3 significant figures is 0.0465.

13

Standard Form

Standard form, or standard index form, is used when writing very small or very large numbers.

In standard form, a number is always written in the following format:

A is always a number between 1 and 10: $1 \leq A < 10$

$$A \times 10^n$$

n tells you how many places you need to move the decimal point.

Converting Numbers into Standard Form

When writing large numbers in standard form, n is always positive.					
8,000,000	=	$8 \times 1,000,000$	=	8×10^6	
45,000,000	=	$4.5 \times 10,000,000$	=	4.5×10^7	
160,000	=	$1.6 \times 100,000$	=	1.6×10^5	

When writing small numbers in standard form, n is always negative.					
0.000465	=	$4.65 \div 10,000$	=	4.65×10^{-4}	
0.009	=	$9 \div 1,000$	=	9.0×10^{-3}	
0.0000077	=	$7.7 \div 1,000,000$	=	7.7×10^{-6}	

Adding or Subtracting Numbers in Standard Form

$$(1.6 \times 10^3) + (2.65 \times 10^4)$$

1 Convert the numbers to ordinary numbers.

$1.6 \times 10^3 = 1,600$
$2.65 \times 10^4 = 26,500$

2 Perform the addition or subtraction.

$1,600 + 26,500 = 28,100$

3 Convert back to standard form.

$28,100 = 2.81 \times 10^4$

Multiplying or Dividing Numbers in Standard Form

$$(6 \times 10^3) \times (4 \times 10^6)$$

1 Multiply or divide the leading numbers and then do the same with the powers of 10.

$6 \times 4 = 24$
$10^3 \times 10^6 = 10^9$

2 Multiply the totals and then convert back to standard form.

$24 \times 10^9 = 24,000,000,000$
$= 2.4 \times 10^{10}$

daydream
EDUCATION

Fractions, Decimals, Percentages

Fractions, decimals and percentages are three different ways of expressing a proportion of a whole.

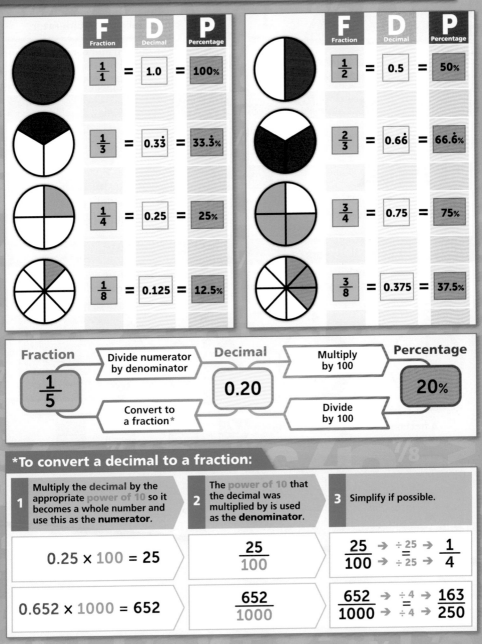

F Fraction	**D** Decimal	**P** Percentage
$\frac{1}{1}$ =	1.0 =	100%
$\frac{1}{3}$ =	0.3̇3̇ =	33.3̇%
$\frac{1}{4}$ =	0.25 =	25%
$\frac{1}{8}$ =	0.125 =	12.5%

F Fraction	**D** Decimal	**P** Percentage
$\frac{1}{2}$ =	0.5 =	50%
$\frac{2}{3}$ =	0.6̇6̇ =	66.6̇%
$\frac{3}{4}$ =	0.75 =	75%
$\frac{3}{8}$ =	0.375 =	37.5%

Fraction — Divide numerator by denominator → **Decimal** — Multiply by 100 → **Percentage**

$\frac{1}{5}$ — 0.20 — 20%

Convert to a fraction* ← Divide by 100

*To convert a decimal to a fraction:

1 Multiply the decimal by the appropriate power of 10 so it becomes a whole number and use this as the **numerator**.

2 The power of 10 that the decimal was multiplied by is used as the **denominator**.

3 Simplify if possible.

$0.25 \times 100 = 25$	$\frac{25}{100}$	$\frac{25}{100} \rightarrow \frac{\div 25}{\div 25} \rightarrow \frac{1}{4}$
$0.652 \times 1000 = 652$	$\frac{652}{1000}$	$\frac{652}{1000} \rightarrow \frac{\div 4}{\div 4} \rightarrow \frac{163}{250}$

Fractions

When a whole or group is divided into equal parts, a fraction is created.

$$\frac{1}{2}$$

⟵ The top number in a fraction is called the **numerator**.

⟵ The bottom number in a fraction is called the **denominator**.

This triangle is split into three equal parts. Each part is one-third.	This square is split into four equal parts. Each part is one-quarter.	This pentagon is split into five equal parts. Each part is one-fifth.
One-third ($\frac{1}{3}$) is purple. Two-thirds ($\frac{2}{3}$) are red.	Three-quarters ($\frac{3}{4}$) are purple. One-quarter ($\frac{1}{4}$) is blue.	Three-fifths ($\frac{3}{5}$) are pink. Two-fifths ($\frac{2}{5}$) are orange.

Equivalent Fractions

Equivalent fractions have different numerators and denominators but are equal in value. They are created by multiplying or dividing both numbers in the fraction by the same number.

$$\frac{1}{2} \quad = \quad \frac{2}{4} \quad = \quad \frac{4}{8}$$

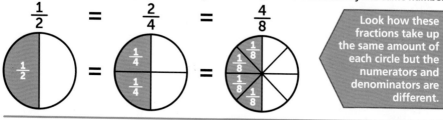

Look how these fractions take up the same amount of each circle but the numerators and denominators are different.

A fraction wall can be used to help identify equivalent fractions.

$$\frac{1}{2} = \frac{4}{8} \qquad \frac{1}{3} = \frac{2}{6}$$

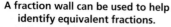

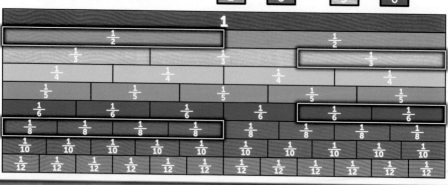

daydream EDUCATION

Finding a Fraction of an Amount

To find a fraction of an amount, divide the **amount** by the bottom number (**denominator**) and then multiply the answer by the top number (**numerator**).

What is $\frac{3}{5}$ of £750?

1 Divide the **amount** by the **denominator**.

$$\frac{750}{5} = 150$$

2 Multiply the answer by the **numerator**.

$$150 \times 3 = 450$$

The above steps can be performed in any order so you can start with whichever operation is easiest.

$\frac{3}{5}$ of £750 is £450

Expressing as a Fraction

To express one amount as a fraction of another amount, follow the steps outlined below.

Write 24 as a fraction of 120.

1 Write the **first number** as the **numerator** and the **second number** as the **denominator**:

$$\frac{24}{120}$$

2 Simplify if possible.

$$\frac{24}{120} \overset{\div 24}{\underset{\div 24}{=}} \frac{1}{5}$$

Write 450 as a fraction of 60.

1 Write the **first number** as the **numerator** and the **second number** as the **denominator**:

$$\frac{450}{60}$$

2 Simplify if possible.

$$\frac{450}{60} \overset{\div 30}{\underset{\div 30}{=}} \frac{15}{2} = 7\frac{1}{2}$$

Simplifying & Ordering Fractions

Simplifying Fractions

To simplify a fraction the **numerator** and **denominator** must be divided by their **highest common factor** (the largest whole number that is a factor of both numbers) to create **like fractions**.

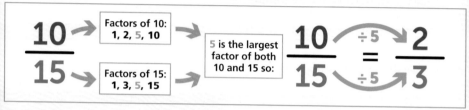

$$\frac{10}{15}$$

Factors of 10:
1, 2, 5, 10

Factors of 15:
1, 3, 5, 15

5 is the largest factor of both 10 and 15 so:

$$\frac{10}{15} \overset{\div 5}{\underset{\div 5}{=}} \frac{2}{3}$$

Simplifying in Steps

Sometimes it is easier to simplify in steps. Divide the top and bottom numbers of the fraction by a common factor until they cannot be divided any further.

$$\frac{60}{100} \overset{\div 10}{\underset{\div 10}{=}} \frac{6}{10} \overset{\div 2}{\underset{\div 2}{=}} \frac{3}{5}$$

Ordering Fractions

It is easy to put **like fractions** (fractions with the same **denominator**) in numerical order.

$$\frac{5}{12} \quad \frac{3}{12} \quad \frac{6}{12} \quad \frac{1}{12} \qquad \Rightarrow \qquad \frac{1}{12} \quad \frac{3}{12} \quad \frac{5}{12} \quad \frac{6}{12}$$

To order fractions with different **denominators**, first change all of the fractions so they have the same **denominator**.

1 Identify the lowest common multiple of the **denominators**. The lowest common multiple of 6, 8 and 4 is 24.

$$\frac{5}{6} \quad \frac{7}{8} \quad \frac{3}{4}$$

Multiples of 6: **6, 12, 18,** 24
Multiples of 8: **8, 16,** 24**, 32**
Multiples of 4: **4, 8, 12, 16, 20,** 24

2 Multiply the fractions by the appropriate numbers so that they share the same **denominator**, 24.

$$\frac{5}{6} \overset{\times 4}{\underset{\times 4}{=}} \frac{20}{24} \qquad \frac{7}{8} \overset{\times 3}{\underset{\times 3}{=}} \frac{21}{24} \qquad \frac{3}{4} \overset{\times 6}{\underset{\times 6}{=}} \frac{18}{24}$$

3 Now that the fractions have the same **denominator**, use the **numerators** to place them in order. Then convert them back to their original form.

$$\frac{18}{24} \quad \frac{20}{24} \quad \frac{21}{24}$$

Smallest ⟶ Largest

Convert back to original form.

$$\frac{3}{4} \quad \frac{5}{6} \quad \frac{7}{8}$$

Smallest ⟶ Largest

daydream
EDUCATION

Mixed Numbers & Improper Fractions

Mixed numbers and improper fractions are two different ways of writing fractions that are greater than one, or a whole.

The fraction below can be written as a mixed number or as an improper fraction.

$=$

Mixed Numbers contain a whole number and a fractional part.

$$1\frac{1}{4}$$

$=$

Improper Fractions have a numerator that is greater than or equal to the denominator.

$$\frac{5}{4}$$

Converting Improper Fractions to Mixed Numbers

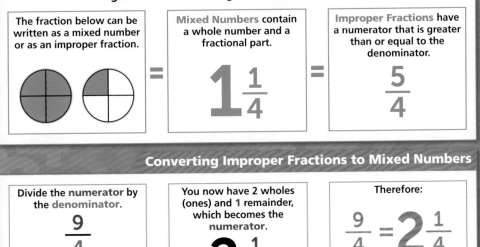

Divide the **numerator** by the **denominator**.

$$\frac{9}{4}$$

4 goes into 9 twice with **1** left over, therefore:

$9 \div 4 = 2$ remainder 1

You now have 2 wholes (ones) and **1** remainder, which becomes the numerator.

$$2\frac{1}{4}$$

The **denominator** does not change.

Therefore:

$$\frac{9}{4} = 2\frac{1}{4}$$

A visual representation of the conversion is shown below.

| 0 | $\frac{1}{4}$ | $\frac{2}{4}$ | $\frac{3}{4}$ | 1 | $\frac{1}{4}$ | $\frac{2}{4}$ | $\frac{3}{4}$ | 2 | $\frac{1}{4}$ | $\frac{2}{4}$ | $\frac{3}{4}$ |

| $\frac{0}{4}$ | $\frac{1}{4}$ | $\frac{2}{4}$ | $\frac{3}{4}$ | $\frac{4}{4}$ | $\frac{5}{4}$ | $\frac{6}{4}$ | $\frac{7}{4}$ | $\frac{8}{4}$ | $\frac{9}{4}$ | $\frac{10}{4}$ | $\frac{11}{4}$ |

Converting Mixed Numbers to Improper Fractions

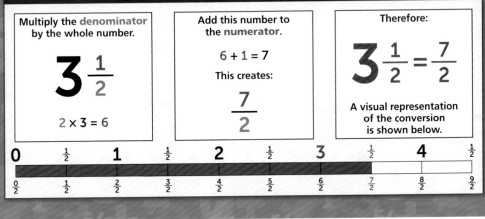

Multiply the **denominator** by the whole number.

$$3\frac{1}{2}$$

$2 \times 3 = 6$

Add this number to the **numerator**.

$6 + 1 = 7$

This creates:

$$\frac{7}{2}$$

Therefore:

$$3\frac{1}{2} = \frac{7}{2}$$

A visual representation of the conversion is shown below.

| 0 | $\frac{1}{2}$ | 1 | $\frac{1}{2}$ | 2 | $\frac{1}{2}$ | 3 | $\frac{1}{2}$ | 4 | $\frac{1}{2}$ |

| $\frac{0}{2}$ | $\frac{1}{2}$ | $\frac{2}{2}$ | $\frac{3}{2}$ | $\frac{4}{2}$ | $\frac{5}{2}$ | $\frac{6}{2}$ | $\frac{7}{2}$ | $\frac{8}{2}$ | $\frac{9}{2}$ |

Adding & Subtracting Fractions

To add or subtract fractions, their **denominators** must be the same. Fractions with the same denominator are known as **like fractions**.

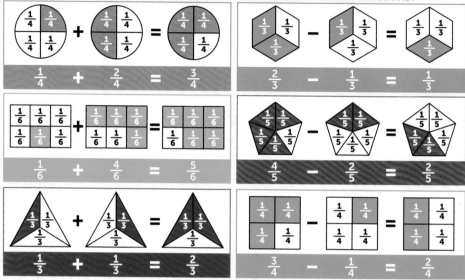

$$\frac{1}{4} + \frac{2}{4} = \frac{3}{4}$$

$$\frac{2}{3} - \frac{1}{3} = \frac{1}{3}$$

$$\frac{1}{6} + \frac{4}{6} = \frac{5}{6}$$

$$\frac{4}{5} - \frac{2}{5} = \frac{2}{5}$$

$$\frac{1}{3} + \frac{1}{3} = \frac{2}{3}$$

$$\frac{3}{4} - \frac{1}{4} = \frac{2}{4}$$

When the denominators are different (known as **unlike fractions**), multiply one or both fractions, so they share the same denominator. To do this, identify the **lowest common multiple** of each denominator.

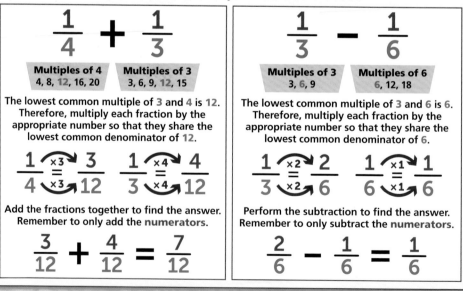

$$\frac{1}{4} + \frac{1}{3}$$

Multiples of 4	Multiples of 3
4, 8, 12, 16, 20	3, 6, 9, 12, 15

The lowest common multiple of 3 and 4 is 12. Therefore, multiply each fraction by the appropriate number so that they share the lowest common denominator of 12.

$$\frac{1}{4} \, \substack{\times 3 \\ = \\ \times 3} \, \frac{3}{12} \qquad \frac{1}{3} \, \substack{\times 4 \\ = \\ \times 4} \, \frac{4}{12}$$

Add the fractions together to find the answer. Remember to only add the **numerators**.

$$\frac{3}{12} + \frac{4}{12} = \frac{7}{12}$$

$$\frac{1}{3} - \frac{1}{6}$$

Multiples of 3	Multiples of 6
3, 6, 9	6, 12, 18

The lowest common multiple of 3 and 6 is 6. Therefore, multiply each fraction by the appropriate number so that they share the lowest common denominator of 6.

$$\frac{1}{3} \, \substack{\times 2 \\ = \\ \times 2} \, \frac{2}{6} \qquad \frac{1}{6} \, \substack{\times 1 \\ = \\ \times 1} \, \frac{1}{6}$$

Perform the subtraction to find the answer. Remember to only subtract the **numerators**.

$$\frac{2}{6} - \frac{1}{6} = \frac{1}{6}$$

Adding Mixed Numbers

To solve this problem, follow the steps outlined below.

$$1\frac{3}{4} + 2\frac{1}{8}$$

1 Change the mixed numbers into improper fractions.

$$1\frac{3}{4} \rightarrow \frac{4}{4} + \frac{3}{4} \rightarrow \frac{7}{4} \qquad 2\frac{1}{8} \rightarrow \frac{8}{8} + \frac{8}{8} + \frac{1}{8} \rightarrow \frac{17}{8}$$

$$\frac{7}{4} + \frac{17}{8}$$

2 If the denominators are different, multiply the fractions so that they share the lowest common denominator.

$$\frac{7}{4} \overset{\times 2}{\underset{\times 2}{=}} \frac{14}{8} \qquad \frac{17}{8}$$

This fraction does not need to change!

3 Add the fractions and then convert the answer back to a mixed number.

8 goes into 31 3 times with 7 remaining, **therefore:**

$$1\frac{3}{4} + 2\frac{1}{8} = 3\frac{7}{8}$$

$$\frac{14}{8} + \frac{17}{8} = \frac{31}{8}$$

$$\frac{31}{8} = 3\frac{7}{8}$$

Subtracting Mixed Numbers

To solve this problem, follow the steps outlined below.

$$2\frac{2}{3} - 1\frac{1}{2}$$

1 Change the mixed numbers into improper fractions.

$$2\frac{2}{3} \rightarrow \frac{3}{3} + \frac{3}{3} + \frac{2}{3} \rightarrow \frac{8}{3} \qquad 1\frac{1}{2} \rightarrow \frac{2}{2} + \frac{1}{2} \rightarrow \frac{3}{2}$$

$$\frac{8}{3} - \frac{3}{2}$$

2 If the denominators are different, multiply the fractions so that they share the lowest common denominator.

$$\frac{8}{3} \overset{\times 2}{\underset{\times 2}{=}} \frac{16}{6} \qquad \frac{3}{2} \overset{\times 3}{\underset{\times 3}{=}} \frac{9}{6}$$

3 Subtract the fraction and then convert the answer back to a mixed number.

6 goes into 7 once with 1 remaining, **therefore:**

$$2\frac{2}{3} - 1\frac{1}{2} = 1\frac{1}{6}$$

$$\frac{16}{6} - \frac{9}{6} = \frac{7}{6}$$

$$\frac{7}{6} = 1\frac{1}{6}$$

Multiplying Fractions

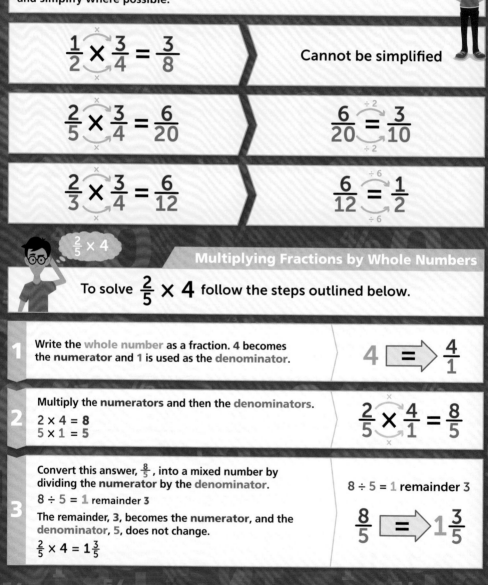

Simplifying Fractions

When multiplying fractions, multiply the **numerators** and the **denominators** and simplify where possible:

$$\frac{1}{2} \times \frac{3}{4} = \frac{3}{8}$$

Cannot be simplified

$$\frac{2}{5} \times \frac{3}{4} = \frac{6}{20}$$

$$\frac{6}{20} \overset{\div 2}{\underset{\div 2}{=}} \frac{3}{10}$$

$$\frac{2}{3} \times \frac{3}{4} = \frac{6}{12}$$

$$\frac{6}{12} \overset{\div 6}{\underset{\div 6}{=}} \frac{1}{2}$$

$\frac{2}{5} \times 4$

Multiplying Fractions by Whole Numbers

To solve $\frac{2}{5} \times 4$ follow the steps outlined below.

1 Write the **whole number** as a fraction. **4** becomes the **numerator** and **1** is used as the **denominator**.

$$4 \implies \frac{4}{1}$$

2 Multiply the **numerators** and then the **denominators**.
$2 \times 4 = \mathbf{8}$
$5 \times 1 = 5$

$$\frac{2}{5} \times \frac{4}{1} = \frac{8}{5}$$

3 Convert this answer, $\frac{8}{5}$, into a mixed number by dividing the **numerator** by the **denominator**.
$8 \div 5 = \mathbf{1}$ remainder **3**

$8 \div 5 = \mathbf{1}$ remainder **3**

The remainder, **3**, becomes the **numerator**, and the **denominator**, **5**, does not change.
$\frac{2}{5} \times 4 = 1\frac{3}{5}$

$$\frac{8}{5} \implies 1\frac{3}{5}$$

daydream EDUCATION

To solve $2\frac{1}{4} \times 3$ follow the steps outlined below.

1 Convert the mixed number into an improper fraction: Multiply the **denominator** by the **whole number**, and add this to the **numerator**.

$2 \times 4 = 8$; $8 + 1$ (the numerator) $= 9$

This is used as the **numerator** in the improper fraction.

$$2\frac{1}{4} \implies \frac{9}{4}$$

2 Write the **whole number** as a fraction. 3 becomes the **numerator** and 1 is the **denominator**.

$$3 \implies \frac{3}{1}$$

3 Multiply the **numerators** and then the **denominators**.

$9 \times 3 = \mathbf{27}$
$4 \times 1 = \mathbf{4}$

$$\frac{9}{4} \times \frac{3}{1} = \frac{27}{4}$$

4 Convert this answer, $\frac{27}{4}$, into a mixed number by dividing the **numerator** by the **denominator**.

$27 \div 4 = 6$ remainder 3

The remainder, **3**, becomes the **numerator**, and the **denominator** does not change.

$2\frac{1}{4} \times 3 = 6\frac{3}{4}$

$27 \div 4 = 6$ remainder 3

$$\frac{27}{4} \implies 6\frac{3}{4}$$

To solve $2\frac{1}{3} \times 1\frac{4}{5}$ follow the steps outlined below.

1 Convert the mixed numbers into improper fractions: Multiply the **denominators** by the **whole numbers** and add the answers to the **numerators**.

$2\frac{1}{3} \rightarrow 3 \times 2 = 6$; $6 + 1$ (the numerator) $= 7$
$1\frac{4}{5} \rightarrow 5 \times 1 = 5$; $5 + 4$ (the numerator) $= 9$

Use the answers as the **numerator** in the fraction.

$$2\frac{1}{3} \implies \frac{7}{3}$$
$$1\frac{4}{5} \implies \frac{9}{5}$$

2 Multiply the **numerators** and then the **denominators**.

$7 \times 9 = \mathbf{63}$
$3 \times 5 = \mathbf{15}$

$$\frac{7}{3} \times \frac{9}{5} = \frac{63}{15}$$

3 Convert the fraction into a mixed number by dividing the **numerator** by the **denominator**.

$63 \div 15 = 4$ remainder 3

The remainder, **3**, becomes the **numerator**, and the **denominator** does not change.

$$\frac{63}{15} \implies 4\frac{3}{15}$$

$4\frac{3}{15}$ can be simplified to $4\frac{1}{5}$

Dividing Fractions

Dividing Fractions

$\frac{1}{2} \div \frac{1}{6}$ is asking how many times $\frac{1}{6}$ goes into $\frac{1}{2}$.
This can be easily identified on a fraction wall.

$\frac{1}{2}$			$\frac{1}{2}$		
$\frac{1}{6}$	$\frac{1}{6}$	$\frac{1}{6}$	$\frac{1}{6}$	$\frac{1}{6}$	$\frac{1}{6}$

$\frac{1}{6}$ goes into $\frac{1}{2}$ three times.

To solve $\frac{4}{7} \div \frac{2}{3}$ follow the steps outlined below.

Step 1

Change the division symbol into a multiplication symbol and turn the **second fraction** upside down.

$$\frac{4}{7} \div \frac{2}{3} \Rightarrow \frac{4}{7} \times \frac{3}{2}$$

Step 2

Multiply the **numerators** together followed by the **denominators**.

$$\frac{4}{7} \times \frac{3}{2} = \frac{12}{14}$$

Step 3

Simplify if possible.

$$\frac{12}{14} \, \overset{\div 2}{\underset{\div 2}{=}} \, \frac{6}{7}$$

Dividing Fractions by Whole Numbers

To divide a fraction by a **whole number**, multiply the **denominator** by the **whole number** and simplify where possible.

$$\frac{1}{2} \div 4 \Rightarrow \frac{1}{2 \times 4} = \frac{1}{8}$$

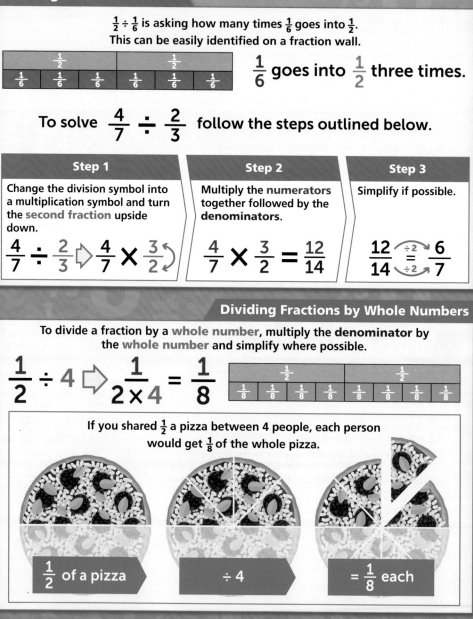

If you shared $\frac{1}{2}$ a pizza between 4 people, each person would get $\frac{1}{8}$ of the whole pizza.

$\frac{1}{2}$ of a pizza   ÷ 4   = $\frac{1}{8}$ each

daydream EDUCATION

Fractions & Recurring Decimals

Terminating and Recurring Decimals

A **terminating decimal** has a finite number of digits. It is a number that ends.

A **recurring decimal** has a digit or group of digits that repeats indefinitely.
The repeating parts are marked by dots above the digits.

$$0.333... = 0.\dot{3} \qquad 0.166... = 0.1\dot{6} \qquad 0.1818... = 0.\dot{1}\dot{8} \qquad 1.752752... = 1.\dot{7}5\dot{2}$$

Fractions with denominators that have **prime factors of only 2 or 5** convert to
terminating decimals. All other fractions convert to recurring decimals.

Fractions & Terminating Decimals			Fractions & Recurring Decimals		
$\frac{1}{2} = 0.5$	$\frac{1}{10} = 0.10$	$\frac{3}{4} = 0.75$	$\frac{2}{3} = 0.\dot{6}$	$\frac{1}{6} = 0.1\dot{6}$	$\frac{1}{11} = 0.\dot{0}\dot{9}$

Converting Recurring Decimals to Fractions

1 Name the decimal.

$$y = 0.\dot{3}2\dot{4}$$

2 Multiply by the relevant power of 10 so the whole recurring unit is to the left of the decimal point.

$$1000y = 324.\dot{3}2\dot{4}$$

3 Subtract the original recurring number (y) to get rid of the decimal digits.

$$\begin{array}{r} 1000y = 324.\dot{3}2\dot{4} \\ - \quad y = 0.\dot{3}2\dot{4} \\ \hline 999y = 324 \end{array}$$

4 Divide by the coefficient of y to leave y, and cancel if possible.

$$y = \frac{324}{999} \overset{\div 27}{\underset{\div 27}{=}} \frac{12}{37}$$

When the recurring part of the decimal number is not directly next to the decimal point, a slightly different method is needed.

1 Label the decimal and multiply it by the relevant power of 10 so the recurring digit is directly to the right of the decimal point.

$$x = 0.1\dot{6}$$
$$10x = 1.\dot{6}$$

2 Multiply the original decimal by the relevant power of 10 so the recurring digit is directly to the left of the decimal point.

$$x = 0.1\dot{6}$$
$$100x = 16.\dot{6}$$

3 Subtract the smaller equation from the larger equation to get rid of the decimal digits.

$$\begin{array}{r} 100x = 16.\dot{6} \\ - \quad 10x = 1.\dot{6} \\ \hline 90x = 15 \end{array}$$

4 Divide by the coefficient of x to leave x, and cancel if possible.

$$x = \frac{15}{90} \overset{\div 15}{\underset{\div 15}{=}} \frac{1}{6}$$

Converting Fractions to Recurring Decimals

To convert from a fraction to a decimal, divide the numerator by the denominator using a calculator or short division.

$$\frac{5}{6} = 6\overline{\smash{)}5.{}^{5}0^{2}0^{2}0^{2}0} = 0.8\,3\,3\,3$$

Measurement

Length

The metric units of length are:
millimetres (mm), **centimetres (cm)**, **metres (m)** and **kilometres (km)**.

10 mm = 1 cm	100 cm = 1 m	1,000 m = 1 km

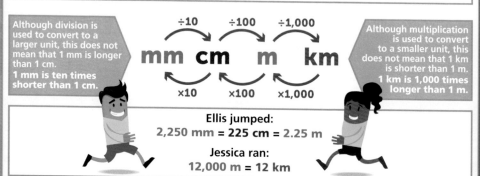

Although division is used to convert to a larger unit, this does not mean that 1 mm is longer than 1 cm.
1 mm is ten times shorter than 1 cm.

÷10   ÷100   ÷1,000

mm cm   m   km

×10   ×100   ×1,000

Although multiplication is used to convert to a smaller unit, this does not mean that 1 km is shorter than 1 m.
1 km is 1,000 times longer than 1 m.

Ellis jumped:
2,250 mm = **225 cm** = 2.25 m

Jessica ran:
12,000 m = 12 km

Mass

The metric units of mass are:
grams (g) and **kilograms (kg)**.

1,000 g = 1 kg

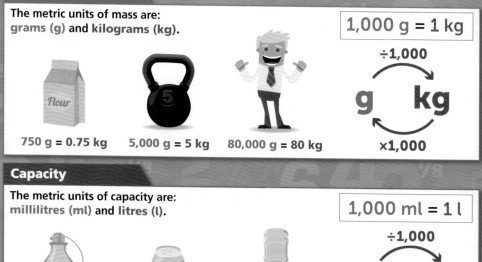

750 g = 0.75 kg   5,000 g = 5 kg   80,000 g = 80 kg

÷1,000

g   kg

×1,000

Capacity

The metric units of capacity are:
millilitres (ml) and **litres (l)**.

1,000 ml = 1 l

100 ml = 0.1 l   330 ml = 0.33 l   20,000 ml = 20 l

÷1,000

ml   l

×1,000

daydream EDUCATION

Area

When converting between units of measurement for area, remember:

$1 \text{ m}^2 = 10,000 \text{ cm}^2$ (100 cm × 100 cm)
1 m^2 is not equal to 100 cm^2

$1 \text{ cm}^2 = 100 \text{ mm}^2$ (10 mm × 10 mm)
1 cm^2 is not equal to 10 mm^2

×100 ×100
$5 \text{ m}^2 = 50,000 \text{ cm}^2$
÷100 ÷100

×10 ×10
$8 \text{ cm}^2 = 800 \text{ mm}^2$
÷10 ÷10

Volume

When converting between units of measurement for volume, remember:

$1 \text{ m}^3 = 1,000,000 \text{ cm}^3$
(100 cm × 100 cm × 100 cm)
1 m^3 is not equal to 100 cm^3

$1 \text{ cm}^3 = 1,000 \text{ mm}^3$
(10 mm × 10 mm × 10 mm)
1 cm^3 is not equal to 10 mm^3

×100 ×100 ×100
$3 \text{ m}^3 = 3,000,000 \text{ cm}^3$
÷100 ÷100 ÷100

×10 ×10 ×10
$8 \text{ cm}^3 = 8,000 \text{ mm}^3$
÷10 ÷10 ÷10

Metric to Imperial Conversions

Length

÷2.54
$2.54 \text{ cm} \approx 1 \text{ in.}$
×2.54

The pen is 12.7 centimetres, or 5 inches, long.

×1.1
$1 \text{ m} \approx 1.1 \text{ yd}$
÷1.1

The pitch is 100 metres, or 110 yards, long.

÷1.6
$1.6 \text{ km} \approx 1 \text{ mi}$
×1.6

It is 184 kilometres, or 115 miles, from Bath to London.

Mass

÷28.35
$28.35 \text{ g} \approx 1 \text{ oz}$
×28.35

The jar holds 340.2 grams, or 12 ounces, of jam.

×2.2
$1 \text{ kg} \approx 2.2 \text{ lb}$
÷2.2

The cat weighs 5 kilograms, or 11 pounds.

÷6.4
$6.4 \text{ kg} \approx 1 \text{ st}$
×6.4

Sally weighs 57.6 kilograms, or 9 stone.

Capacity

÷568
$568 \text{ ml} \approx 1 \text{ pt}$
×568

The jug has a capacity of 1,136 millilitres, or 2 pints.

×1.76
$1 \text{ l} \approx 1.76 \text{ pt}$
÷1.76

The carton has a capacity of 2 litres, or 3.52 pints.

÷4.5
$4.5 \text{ l} \approx 1 \text{ gal.}$
×4.5

The bath has a capacity of 180 litres, or 40 gallons.

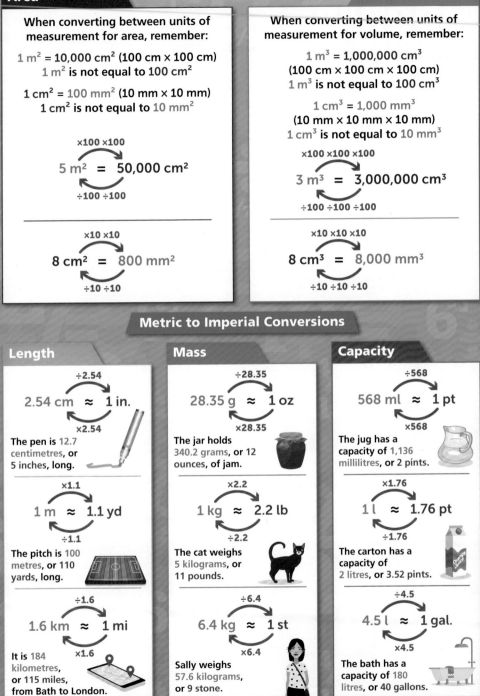

daydream EDUCATION

27

Algebra

In algebra, letters (**variables**) can be used to represent unknown numerical values. For example, in the equation $3x + y = 16$, x and y are variables.

Key Terminology

A **term** is a collection of numbers and letters. Terms are separated by mathematical symbols.	$3x + 4xy = 18 + y$
An **expression** includes terms and operational (mathematical) symbols but not the equals symbol.	$2x + 5y - 2$
An **equation** is made up of two expressions that are equal.	$4x + 5y = 23$
An **identity** is an equation that is true for all values of the variables. $3x = 12$ is not an identity as it is only true when $x = 4$.	$2y = y + y$

Simplifying Algebraic Expressions

To simplify algebraic expressions, like terms can be collected together. Like terms contain the **same variable** raised to the **same power**.

Addition and Subtraction

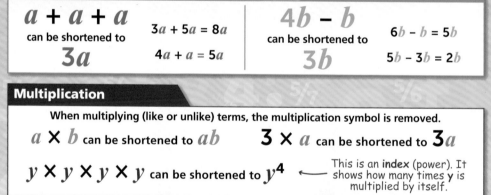

$a + a + a$ can be shortened to $3a$

$3a + 5a = 8a$

$4a + a = 5a$

$4b - b$ can be shortened to $3b$

$6b - b = 5b$

$5b - 3b = 2b$

Multiplication

When multiplying (like or unlike) terms, the multiplication symbol is removed.

$a \times b$ can be shortened to ab

$3 \times a$ can be shortened to $3a$

$y \times y \times y \times y$ can be shortened to y^4 ← This is an **index** (power). It shows how many times y is multiplied by itself.

Remember $4y$ is not the same as y^4.

$4y = y + y + y + y$

$y^4 = y \times y \times y \times y$

Division

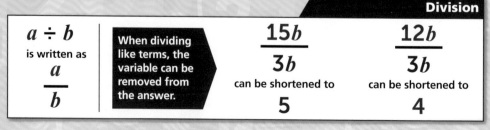

$a \div b$ is written as $\dfrac{a}{b}$

When dividing like terms, the variable can be removed from the answer.

$\dfrac{15b}{3b}$ can be shortened to 5

$\dfrac{12b}{3b}$ can be shortened to 4

daydream EDUCATION

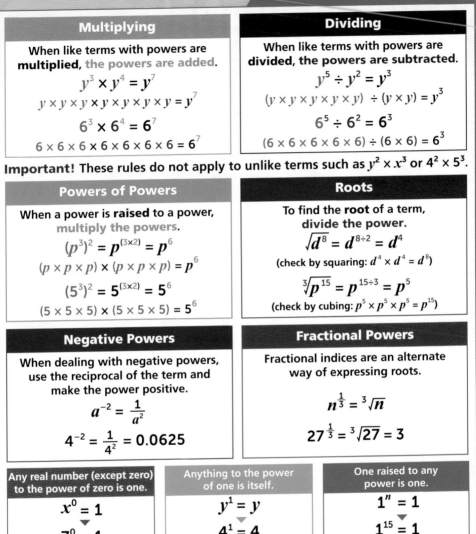

Multiplying

When like terms with powers are **multiplied**, the powers are added.

$$y^3 \times y^4 = y^7$$

$$y \times y \times y \times y \times y \times y \times y = y^7$$

$$6^3 \times 6^4 = 6^7$$

$$6 \times 6 \times 6 \times 6 \times 6 \times 6 \times 6 = 6^7$$

Dividing

When like terms with powers are **divided, the powers are subtracted.**

$$y^5 \div y^2 = y^3$$

$$(y \times y \times y \times y \times y) \div (y \times y) = y^3$$

$$6^5 \div 6^2 = 6^3$$

$$(6 \times 6 \times 6 \times 6 \times 6) \div (6 \times 6) = 6^3$$

Important! These rules do not apply to unlike terms such as $y^2 \times x^3$ or $4^2 \times 5^3$.

Powers of Powers

When a power is **raised** to a power, multiply the powers.

$$(p^3)^2 = p^{(3 \times 2)} = p^6$$

$$(p \times p \times p) \times (p \times p \times p) = p^6$$

$$(5^3)^2 = 5^{(3 \times 2)} = 5^6$$

$$(5 \times 5 \times 5) \times (5 \times 5 \times 5) = 5^6$$

Roots

To find the **root** of a term, divide the power.

$$\sqrt{d^8} = d^{8 \div 2} = d^4$$

(check by squaring: $d^4 \times d^4 = d^8$)

$$\sqrt[3]{p^{15}} = p^{15 \div 3} = p^5$$

(check by cubing: $p^5 \times p^5 \times p^5 = p^{15}$)

Negative Powers

When dealing with negative powers, use the reciprocal of the term and make the power positive.

$$a^{-2} = \frac{1}{a^2}$$

$$4^{-2} = \frac{1}{4^2} = 0.0625$$

Fractional Powers

Fractional indices are an alternate way of expressing roots.

$$n^{\frac{1}{3}} = \sqrt[3]{n}$$

$$27^{\frac{1}{3}} = \sqrt[3]{27} = 3$$

Any real number (except zero) to the power of zero is one.

$$x^0 = 1$$

$$7^0 = 1$$

Anything to the power of one is itself.

$$y^1 = y$$

$$4^1 = 4$$

One raised to any power is one.

$$1^n = 1$$

$$1^{15} = 1$$

Examples

Expression	Like?	Why?	Simplified
$3b + 2b$	Yes	Same variable	$5b$
$x + x^4$	No	Variables raised to different powers	
$2ab + 2ba$	Yes	Same variables	$4ab$
$2y + y^2 - 4$	No	Variables raised to different powers	
$2x^2 - 4x - x^2 + 2x$	Yes	Same variables and powers	$x^2 - 2x$

Solving Equations

There is not one simple rule to follow when solving equations. However, the aim is to get the **variable** by itself on one side of the equation with a **number** on the other side – for example, $x = 2$. Look at how the equations below have been rearranged and solved by using inverse operations to 'undo' the equation.

$$n + 3 = 12$$
$$\boxed{-3} \quad \boxed{-3}$$
$$n = 9$$

$$\frac{12}{w} = 3$$
$$\boxed{\times w} \quad \boxed{\times w}$$
$$12 = 3w$$
$$\boxed{\div 3} \quad \boxed{\div 3}$$
$$4 = w$$

$$3x + 4 = x + 6$$
$$\boxed{-4} \quad \boxed{-4}$$
$$3x = x + 2$$
$$\boxed{-x} \quad \boxed{-x}$$
$$2x = 2$$
$$\boxed{\div 2} \quad \boxed{\div 2}$$
$$x = 1$$

Equations can help solve real-life problems.

Rohan has three pieces of wood of equal length, and one 6 cm piece. The total length of the four pieces of wood is 42 cm. How long is each of the three equal pieces of wood?

1. Turn the question into an equation.

Use w to represent the unknown value (the length of the three equal pieces of wood).	3 pieces of wood	Other piece of wood	Total length
	$3 \times w$	$+ \quad 6$	$= \quad 42$

2. Solve the equation to find the value of w.

Subtraction is the inverse operation of addition so **subtract 6 from both sides of the equation.**	$3w$	$+ \quad 6$ -6	$= \quad 42$ -6
Division is the inverse operation of multiplication so **divide both sides of the equation by 3.**	$3w$ $\div 3$ w		$= \quad 36$ $\div 3$ $= \quad 12$

The equation is now solved: $w = 12$. Each equal piece of wood is 12 cm long.

Equations Involving Brackets

When an equation contains brackets, the brackets need to be expanded (multiplied out) before the equation can be rearranged and solved.

$$3(y + 6) = 2(y - 3)$$
$$3y + 18 = 2y - 6$$
$$\quad -18 \quad -18$$
$$3y = 2y - 24$$
$$\quad -2y \quad -2y$$
$$y = -24$$

daydream
EDUCATION

Equations Involving Fractions

When an equation contains fractions, the fractions need to be removed.

To remove fractions, multiply all terms in the equation by the **denominators** in the fractions.

The equations can then be solved.

Multiply everything by the denominator (3).	$$4 - \frac{x}{3} = 1$$ $$3(4) - \frac{3(x)}{3} = 3(1)$$
Then simplify and solve.	$$12 - \frac{\cancel{3}(x)}{\cancel{3}} = 3$$ $$12 - x = 3$$ $$\underset{+x \quad +x}{}$$ $$12 = 3 + x$$ $$\underset{-3 \quad -3}{}$$ $$9 = x$$

When there are two fractions, multiply everything by both denominators.

Multiply everything by both denominators (3 and 5).	$$\frac{x}{3} + \frac{x-2}{5} = 6$$ $$\frac{3 \times 5 \times (x)}{3} + \frac{3 \times 5 \times (x-2)}{5} = 3 \times 5 \times 6$$
Then simplify and solve.	$$\frac{\cancel{3} \times 5 \times (x)}{\cancel{3}} + \frac{3 \times \cancel{5} \times (x-2)}{\cancel{5}} = 90$$ $$5x + 3(x - 2) = 90$$ $$5x + 3x - 6 = 90$$ $$8x - 6 = 90$$ $$\underset{+6 \quad +6}{}$$ $$8x = 96$$ $$\underset{\div 8 \quad \div 8}{}$$ $$x = 12$$

Equations Involving Squares

Equations that contain squared terms are called quadratic equations. To solve quadratic equations, you will need to take the square root of both sides of the equation as the last step.

Most quadratic equations are more complex than this example and need to be solved using different methods, such as factorising and completing the square.

The two solutions to this equation are 3 and –3.

$$11y^2 + 5 = 104$$
$$\underset{-5 \qquad -5}{}$$
$$11y^2 = 99$$
$$\underset{\div 11 \qquad \div 11}{}$$
$$y^2 = 9$$
$$\underset{\sqrt{} \qquad \sqrt{}}{}$$
$$y = \pm 3$$

Expanding and Factorising

To expand brackets, multiply everything inside the brackets by the coefficient outside the brackets. This is often taught using two different methods:

The Claw Method	The Grid Method

The Claw Method

$$3(x + 4)$$
$$= (3 \times x) + (3 \times 4)$$
$$= 3x + 12$$

The Grid Method

$3(x + 4)$

×	x	$+4$
3	$3x$	12

$$= 3x + 12$$

When the term outside the brackets includes a coefficient and a variable, multiply everything inside the brackets by the coefficient and the variable.

$$2z(4x - 2y)$$
$$= (2z \times 4x) + (2z \times -2y)$$
$$= 8xz - 4yz$$

$2z(4x - 2y)$

×	$4x$	$-2y$
$2z$	$8xz$	$-4yz$

$$= 8xz - 4yz$$

Sometimes you will need to expand two brackets and simplify.

1. Expand each of the brackets.
2. Simplify where possible by collecting like terms.

$$4(a + 6) + 5(2a - 3)$$
$$= (4 \times a) + (4 \times 6) + (5 \times 2a) + (5 \times -3)$$
$$= 4a + 24 + 10a - 15$$
$$= 14a + 9$$

To expand double brackets, multiply every term in the first bracket by every term in the second bracket. The example below uses the grid method.

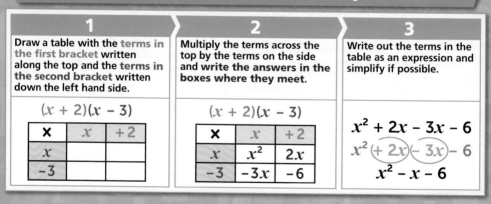

1	2	3
Draw a table with the **terms in the first bracket** written along the top and the **terms in the second bracket** written down the left hand side.	Multiply the terms across the top by the terms on the side and write the answers in the boxes where they meet.	Write out the terms in the table as an expression and simplify if possible.

$(x + 2)(x - 3)$

×	x	$+2$
x		
-3		

$(x + 2)(x - 3)$

×	x	$+2$
x	x^2	$2x$
-3	$-3x$	-6

$$x^2 + 2x - 3x - 6$$
$$x^2 + 2x - 3x - 6$$
$$x^2 - x - 6$$

 daydream EDUCATION

Factorise - Back to Brackets

Factoring is the opposite of expanding. It involves introducing a bracket to an expression.

EXPAND

$$a(a - 3) = a^2 - 3a$$

FACTORISE

To factorise this expression, follow the steps outlined below.

$$3x - 9$$

1 Identify the Highest Common Factor (HCF) of the terms in the expression.

The HCF of $3x$ and -9 is 3.

$$3x - 9$$

Factors of $3x$:	Factors of -9:
1, 3	1, 3, 9

2 List this (3) outside the bracket.

Then divide the original terms ($3x$ and -9) by this number and place the answers within the brackets.

$$3x - 9$$
$$\div 3 \qquad \div 3$$
$$3(x - 3)$$

3 Check your answer by expanding the bracket.

$$3(x - 3)$$
$$= (3 \times x) - (3 \times -3)$$
$$= 3x - 9$$

To factorise this expression, follow the steps outlined below.

$$12x^2 + 16xy$$

1 Identify the HCF of the terms in the expression.

The HCF of $12x^2$ and $16xy$ is $4x$.

$$12x^2 + 16xy$$

Factors of $12x^2$:	Factors of $16xy$:
$1x, 2x, 3x, 4x, 6x...$	$1x, 2x, 4x, 8x...$

2 List this ($4x$) outside the bracket.

Then divide the original terms ($12x^2$ and $16xy$) by this number and place the answers within the brackets.

$$12x^2 + 16xy$$
$$\div 4x \qquad \div 4x$$
$$4x(3x + 4y)$$

3 Check your answer by expanding the bracket.

$$4x(3x + 4y)$$
$$= (4x \times 3x) + (4x \times 4y)$$
$$= 12x^2 + 16xy$$

Substitution

When substituting in sport, one player is swapped for another. The same principle applies in algebra - a variable (letter) is swapped with a value.

What is the value of $3x + 7$ when $x = 4$?

$$3x + 7 = (3 \times x) + 7$$
$$= (3 \times 4) + 7$$
$$= 12 + 7$$
$$= 19$$

What is the value of $y^2 - 2y$ when $y = 3$?

$$y^2 - 2y = (y \times y) - (2 \times y)$$
$$= (3 \times 3) - (2 \times 3)$$
$$= 9 - 6$$
$$= 3$$

Sometimes, solving a problem involves substituting numbers into a formula.

Will gets paid **£15** an hour. If he works for **6** hours, how much does he get paid?

Total Pay = Hours × Wage

1 Substitute the known numbers into the formula.

Total Pay = 6 × £15

2 Follow the rules of **BIDMAS** to find the answer.

Total Pay = £90

Convert **86°F** from Fahrenheit to Celsius.

$$C = \frac{5(f - 32)}{9}$$

1 Substitute the known numbers into the formula.

$$C = \frac{5(86 - 32)}{9}$$

2 Follow the rules of **BIDMAS** to find the answer.

$$C = \frac{5(54)}{9} \blacktriangleright C = \frac{270}{9} \blacktriangleright C = 30$$

The cooking time for a chicken is 30 minutes per kilogram (kg), plus 40 minutes. What is the cooking time for a chicken that weighs 1.5 kg?

Cooking Time = 30 × weight + 40
$$T = 30w + 40$$

1 Substitute the known numbers into the formula.

$$T = (30 \times 1.5) + 40$$

2 Follow the rules of **BIDMAS** to find the answer.

$$T = 45 + 40$$
$$= 85$$

34

daydream EDUCATION

Rearranging Formulae

A **formula** is an **equation** that shows the relationship between different variables.

Sometimes you can rearrange formulae using inverse operations to make them easier to work with and solve. In the examples below, the equations have been rearranged to make x the subject:

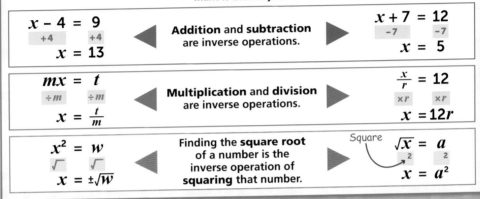

$$x - 4 = 9$$
$+4 \qquad +4$
$$x = 13$$

Addition and **subtraction** are inverse operations.

$$x + 7 = 12$$
$-7 \qquad -7$
$$x = 5$$

$$mx = t$$
$\div m \qquad \div m$
$$x = \frac{t}{m}$$

Multiplication and **division** are inverse operations.

$$\frac{x}{r} = 12$$
$\times r \qquad \times r$
$$x = 12r$$

$$x^2 = w$$
$\sqrt{} \qquad \sqrt{}$
$$x = \pm\sqrt{w}$$

Finding the **square root** of a number is the inverse operation of **squaring** that number.

Square
$$\sqrt{x} = a$$
$2 \qquad 2$
$$x = a^2$$

In exams, you will often be asked to rearrange formulae so they can be solved.

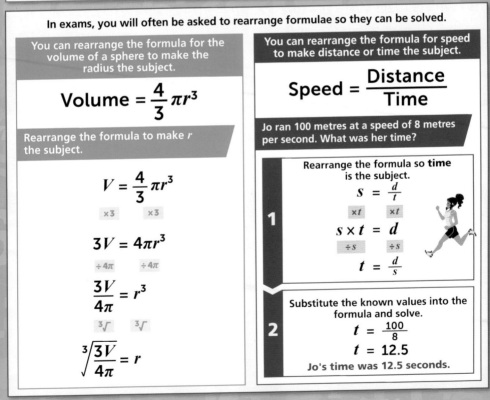

You can rearrange the formula for the volume of a sphere to make the radius the subject.

$$\text{Volume} = \frac{4}{3}\pi r^3$$

Rearrange the formula to make r the subject.

$$V = \frac{4}{3}\pi r^3$$
$\times 3 \qquad \times 3$

$$3V = 4\pi r^3$$
$\div 4\pi \qquad \div 4\pi$

$$\frac{3V}{4\pi} = r^3$$
$\sqrt[3]{} \qquad \sqrt[3]{}$

$$\sqrt[3]{\frac{3V}{4\pi}} = r$$

You can rearrange the formula for speed to make distance or time the subject.

$$\text{Speed} = \frac{\text{Distance}}{\text{Time}}$$

Jo ran 100 metres at a speed of 8 metres per second. What was her time?

1 Rearrange the formula so **time** is the subject.
$$s = \frac{d}{t}$$
$\times t \qquad \times t$
$$s \times t = d$$
$\div s \qquad \div s$
$$t = \frac{d}{s}$$

2 Substitute the known values into the formula and solve.
$$t = \frac{100}{8}$$
$$t = 12.5$$
Jo's time was 12.5 seconds.

Manipulating Surds

Surds are irrational numbers that involve roots (e.g. $\sqrt{2}$ and $\sqrt[3]{5}$).

Rational numbers are numbers than can be written as a fraction $\frac{a}{b}$, where a and b are integers with no common factor ($b \neq 0$), such as 3, $\frac{7}{9}$ and -6.

Consequently, **irrational numbers** are numbers that cannot be written as a fraction $\frac{a}{b}$, where a and b are integers with no common factor ($b \neq 0$), such as π, $\sqrt{2}$ and $\sqrt[3]{5}$.

Simplifying Expressions Involving Surds

Where a, b are positive real numbers.

$$\sqrt{a} \times \sqrt{b} = \sqrt{ab}$$
$$\sqrt{3} \times \sqrt{2} = \sqrt{3 \times 2} = \sqrt{6}$$

$$\sqrt{(ab)} = \sqrt{a} \times \sqrt{b}$$
$$\sqrt{(75)} = \sqrt{25} \times \sqrt{3}$$
$$\sqrt{75} = 5\sqrt{3}$$

$$(\sqrt{a})^2 = \sqrt{a} \times \sqrt{a} = a$$
$$(\sqrt{6})^2 = \sqrt{6} \times \sqrt{6} = 6$$

$$\frac{\sqrt{a}}{\sqrt{b}} = \sqrt{\frac{a}{b}}$$
$$\frac{\sqrt{6}}{\sqrt{3}} = \sqrt{\frac{6}{3}} = \sqrt{2}$$

$$(a + \sqrt{b})^2 = (a + \sqrt{b})(a + \sqrt{b}) = a^2 + 2a\sqrt{b} + b$$
$$(5 + \sqrt{2})^2 = (5 + \sqrt{2})(5 + \sqrt{2}) = 25 + 10\sqrt{2} + 2$$
Can be simplified to $27 + 10\sqrt{2}$

$$(a + \sqrt{b})(a - \sqrt{b}) = a^2 + a\sqrt{b} - a\sqrt{b} - (\sqrt{b})^2 = a^2 - b$$
$$(7 + \sqrt{2})(7 - \sqrt{2}) = 7^2 + 7\sqrt{2} - 7\sqrt{2} - (\sqrt{2})^2 = 49 - 2$$
Can be simplified to 47

Remember:

$$\sqrt{(a + b)} \neq \sqrt{a} + \sqrt{b} \qquad \sqrt{(a - b)} \neq \sqrt{a} - \sqrt{b}$$

Rationalising

An important process used in maths is rationalising the denominator. This makes the denominator of a fraction rational.

For denominators of the form $a \pm \sqrt{b}$, you need to change the sign in front of the root (see example below).

$$\frac{a}{\sqrt{b}} = \frac{a}{\sqrt{b}} \times \frac{\sqrt{b}}{\sqrt{b}} = \frac{a\sqrt{b}}{b}$$

$$\frac{2}{\sqrt{3}} = \frac{2}{\sqrt{3}} \times \frac{\sqrt{3}}{\sqrt{3}} = \frac{2\sqrt{3}}{3}$$

Rationalising Example

$$\frac{4}{(3 + \sqrt{5})} = \frac{4(3 - \sqrt{5})}{(3 + \sqrt{5})(3 - \sqrt{5})}$$
Change the sign.

$$= \frac{4(3 - \sqrt{5})}{9 - 3\sqrt{5} + 3\sqrt{5} - (\sqrt{5})^2}$$

$$= \frac{4(3 - \sqrt{5})}{9 - 5}$$

$$= \frac{4(3 - \sqrt{5})}{4}$$

$$= 3 - \sqrt{5}$$

Simplifying Example

$$\sqrt{12} + \sqrt{27}$$

$$\sqrt{12} = \sqrt{4} \times \sqrt{3} = 2\sqrt{3} \qquad \sqrt{27} = \sqrt{9} \times \sqrt{3} = 3\sqrt{3}$$

$$= 2\sqrt{3} + 3\sqrt{3}$$

$$= 5\sqrt{3}$$

daydream
EDUCATION

Algebraic Fractions

Simplifying

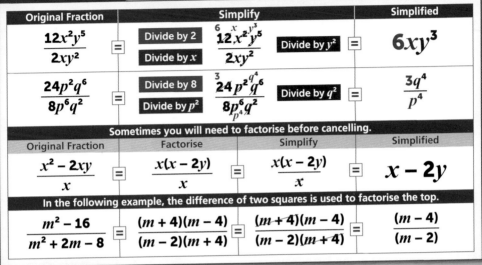

Original Fraction		Simplify				Simplified
$\dfrac{12x^2y^5}{2xy^2}$	$=$	Divide by 2 / Divide by x	$\dfrac{12x^{2}y^{3}}{2xy^2}$	Divide by y^2	$=$	$6xy^3$
$\dfrac{24p^2q^6}{8p^6q^2}$	$=$	Divide by 8 / Divide by p^2	$\dfrac{24p^2q^4}{8p^4q^2}$	Divide by q^2	$=$	$\dfrac{3q^4}{p^4}$

Sometimes you will need to factorise before cancelling.

Original Fraction		Factorise		Simplify		Simplified
$\dfrac{x^2 - 2xy}{x}$	$=$	$\dfrac{x(x - 2y)}{x}$	$=$	$\dfrac{x(x - 2y)}{x}$	$=$	$x - 2y$

In the following example, the difference of two squares is used to factorise the top.

$\dfrac{m^2 - 16}{m^2 + 2m - 8}$	$=$	$\dfrac{(m + 4)(m - 4)}{(m - 2)(m + 4)}$	$=$	$\dfrac{(m + 4)(m - 4)}{(m - 2)(m + 4)}$	$=$	$\dfrac{(m - 4)}{(m - 2)}$

Multiplying and Dividing

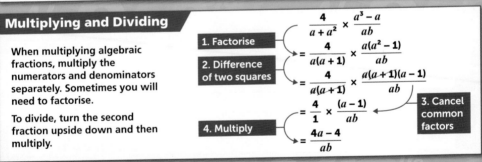

When multiplying algebraic fractions, multiply the numerators and denominators separately. Sometimes you will need to factorise.

To divide, turn the second fraction upside down and then multiply.

1. Factorise

2. Difference of two squares

3. Cancel common factors

4. Multiply

$$\frac{4}{a + a^2} \times \frac{a^3 - a}{ab}$$

$$= \frac{4}{a(a + 1)} \times \frac{a(a^2 - 1)}{ab}$$

$$= \frac{4}{a(a + 1)} \times \frac{a(a + 1)(a - 1)}{ab}$$

$$= \frac{4}{1} \times \frac{(a - 1)}{ab}$$

$$= \frac{4a - 4}{ab}$$

Adding and Subtracting

	$\dfrac{m + 2}{2} - \dfrac{m - 1}{3}$	$\dfrac{3}{x + 3} + \dfrac{1}{x - 2}$
Find the lowest common denominator (LCD) of both fractions and then multiply the fractions so they share the LCD.	$= \dfrac{3(m + 2)}{6} - \dfrac{2(m - 1)}{6}$	$= \dfrac{3(x - 2)}{(x + 3)(x - 2)} + \dfrac{(x + 3)}{(x + 3)(x - 2)}$
Rewrite the fractions as one fraction.	$= \dfrac{3(m + 2) - 2(m - 1)}{6}$	$= \dfrac{3(x - 2) + (x + 3)}{(x + 3)(x - 2)}$
Expand the brackets.	$= \dfrac{3m + 6 - 2m + 2}{6}$	$= \dfrac{3x - 6 + x + 3}{(x + 3)(x - 2)}$
Simplify.	$= \dfrac{m + 8}{6}$	$= \dfrac{4x - 3}{(x + 3)(x - 2)}$

Factorising Quadratic Equations

Quadratic expressions and equations contain one or more squared terms (x^2).
The standard form of a quadratic equation is $ax^2 + bx + c = 0$.

Before solving quadratic equations always rearrange them into the form:

$$ax^2 + bx + c = 0$$

$$2n^2 = 6n - 8$$
$$\underset{-6n}{} \quad \underset{-6n}{}$$
$$2n^2 - 6n = -8$$
$$\underset{+8}{} \quad \underset{+8}{}$$
$$2n^2 - 6n + 8 = 0$$

Some quadratic equations of the form $ax^2 + bx + c = 0$ (where $a = 1$) can be solved by factorising.

$$x^2 + 7x + 6 = 0$$

1 Find the factor pairs of c (+ 6).
1 and 6 are a factor pair of 6.
2 and 3 are a factor pair of 6.

$$1 \times 6 = 6$$
$$2 \times 3 = 6$$

2 Identify if any of the factor pairs can be added together to equal b (+ 7).

$$2 + 3 = 5 \quad ✗$$
$$6 + 1 = 7 \quad ✓$$

3 Split x^2 into its factors and place them inside two brackets.

$$x^2$$
$$(x \quad)(x \quad)$$

4 Place each of the numbers from the factor pair into the separate brackets (including the correct symbols).

$$+6 \qquad +1$$
$$(x + 6)(x + 1)$$

$x^2 + 7x + 6 = 0$ can be factorised to $(x + 6)(x + 1) = 0$
so the solutions are: $x = -6$, $x = -1$

Remember to check your answer by expanding the brackets.

The **difference of two squares rule** is used to factorise quadratic expressions in which one squared number is subtracted from another.

$$a^2 - b^2$$
$$(a - b)(a + b)$$

Look at how the following expressions can be factorised using the difference of two squares rule:	$p^2 - 36$	$y^2 - 25$	$25m^2 - 9n^2$
	▼	▼	▼
	$= (p - 6)(p + 6)$	$= (y - 5)(y + 5)$	$= (5m - 3n)(5m + 3n)$

daydream EDUCATION

The Quadratic Formula

A quadratic equation, in the form $ax^2 + bx + c = 0$, can be solved by using the quadratic formula, regardless of whether the expression can be factorised.

You will need to use the quadratic formula when you have a quadratic that does not factorise easily or a question that asks for decimal places (d.p.), exact answers or surds.

The ± sign means that there will be two solutions.

$$x = \frac{-b \pm \sqrt{b^2 - 4ac}}{2a}$$

To solve this equation, follow the steps outlined below.

$$2x^2 - 3x = 7$$

1 Rearrange the formula into the form $ax^2 + bx + c = 0$.

$$2x^2 - 3x = 7$$
$$\quad -7 \qquad\qquad -7$$
$$2x^2 - 3x - 7 = 0$$

2 Identify the values of a, b and c, and substitute into the quadratic formula.

$$x = \frac{-b \pm \sqrt{b^2 - 4ac}}{2a}$$

$$x = \frac{-(-3) \pm \sqrt{(-3)^2 - 4(2)(-7)}}{2(2)}$$

3 Simplify in stages.

$$x = \frac{-(-3) \pm \sqrt{(-3)^2 - 4(2)(-7)}}{2(2)}$$

$$x = \frac{3 \pm \sqrt{9 - -56}}{4}$$

$$x = \frac{3 \pm \sqrt{65}}{4}$$

4 Solve for both + and –.

$$x = \frac{3 + \sqrt{65}}{4} \qquad\qquad x = \frac{3 - \sqrt{65}}{4}$$
$$x = 2.77 \text{ (2 d.p.)} \qquad x = -1.27 \text{ (2 d.p.)}$$

Remember to check your answers by substituting the values into the original equation and solving.

 daydream EDUCATION

Photocopying or scanning this image is a breach of copyright law.

39

Completing the Square

Quadratics can be rearranged and solved by making the parts of the expression containing x-terms into a 'perfect square'.

Before completing the square, ensure the quadratic is of the form: $ax^2 + bx + c = 0$.

To solve $x^2 + 6x + 4 = 0$, follow the steps outlined below.

1 Make the $ax^2 + bx$ part of the equation into the form $(x + \frac{b}{2})^2$.

$$x^2 + 6x + 4 = 0$$
$$(x + \tfrac{6}{2})^2 = (x + 3)^2$$

2 If you expand $(x + 3)^2$ you will notice that you have **added 9** to the equation. Therefore, to ensure the overall value of the equation does not change, **9 needs to be subtracted** outside of the brackets.

	x	$+3$
x	x^2	$3x$
$+3$	$3x$	9

$$(x + 3)^2 + 4 - 9 = 0$$

3 Simplify where possible and solve.

$$(x + 3)^2 - 5 = 0$$
$$(x + 3)^2 = 5$$
$$x + 3 = \pm\sqrt{5}$$
$$x = \pm\sqrt{5} - 3$$

In surd form the solutions are: $x = \sqrt{5} - 3$ and $x = -\sqrt{5} - 3$.
In number form, the solutions are approximately: −0.76 and −5.24 (both answers to 2 d.p.).

When $a \neq 1$, you must factor out the coefficient of x^2 before solving.

To solve $2x^2 - 8x + 5 = 0$, follow the steps outlined below.

1 Factor out the coefficient of x^2 by taking out a factor of 2.

$$2x^2 - 8x + 5 = 0$$
$$2(x^2 - 4x) + 5 = 0$$

2 Make the $ax^2 + bx$ part of the equation into the form $(x + \frac{b}{2})^2$.

$$2(x^2 - 4x) + 5 = 0$$
$$2(x + \tfrac{-4}{2})^2 = 2(x - 2)^2$$

3 If you expand $2(x - 2)^2$ you will notice that you have **added 8** to the equation. Therefore, to ensure the overall value of the equation does not change, **8 needs to be subtracted** outside of the brackets.

$$2(x - 2)^2$$
$$= 2(x^2 - 4x + 4)$$
$$= 2x^2 - 8x + 8$$
$$2(x - 2)^2 + 5 - 8 = 0$$

4 Simplify where possible and solve.

$$2(x - 2)^2 - 3 = 0$$
$$2(x - 2)^2 = 3$$
$$(x - 2)^2 = \tfrac{3}{2}$$
$$x - 2 = \pm\sqrt{\tfrac{3}{2}}$$
$$x = \pm\sqrt{\tfrac{3}{2}} + 2$$

In surd form, the solutions are: $x = -\sqrt{\tfrac{3}{2}} + 2$ and $x = \sqrt{\tfrac{3}{2}} + 2$.

daydream
EDUCATION

To express $2x^2 + 6x + 7$ in the form $a(x + m)^2 + n$, follow the steps below.

1 Factor out the coefficient of x^2 by taking out a factor of 2.

$$2x^2 + 6x + 7$$
$$2(x^2 + 3x) + 7$$

2 Make the $ax^2 + bx$ part of the expression into the form $a(x + \frac{b}{2})^2$.

$$2(x^2 + 3x) + 7$$
$$2(x + \tfrac{3}{2})^2$$

3 If you expand $2(x + \frac{3}{2})^2$ you will notice that $\frac{9}{2}$ has been added to the expression. Therefore, to ensure the overall value of the expression does not change, $\frac{9}{2}$ needs to be subtracted.

$$2(x + \tfrac{3}{2})^2$$
$$= 2(x^2 + 3x + \tfrac{9}{4}) \quad \text{Simplified from } \tfrac{18}{4}.$$
$$= 2x^2 + 6x + \tfrac{9}{2}$$
- - - - - - - - - - - - - - - - - - - -
$$2(x + \tfrac{3}{2})^2 + 7 - \tfrac{9}{2}$$

4 Simplify where possible.

$$2(x + \tfrac{3}{2})^2 + 7 - \tfrac{9}{2}$$
$$2(x + \tfrac{3}{2})^2 + \tfrac{14}{2} - \tfrac{9}{2}$$
$$2(x + \tfrac{3}{2})^2 + \tfrac{5}{2}$$

Therefore, $2x^2 + 6x + 7$ expressed in the form $a(x + m)^2 + n$ is $2(x + \frac{3}{2})^2 + \frac{5}{2}$

Sketching Graphs

Expressing a quadratic in the form $a(x + m)^2 + n$ can help you identify key information about the graph, such as the turning point.

Example

Expressing $x^2 + 8x + 5$ in the form $a(x + m)^2 + n$ by completing the square will help you determine the turning point of the graph.

$$x^2 + 8x + 5 \implies (x + 4)^2 - 11$$

The **x-coordinate** of the turning point (minimum or maximum) occurs when the brackets are equal to 0 so if $m = 4$, $x = -4$: $(-4 + 4)^2 = 0$

The **y-coordinate** of the turning point (minimum or maximum point) is equal to the value of n: -11.

If a and n are both positive, the graph will never cross the x-axis, and the quadratic will have no real roots.

The turning point (minimum) of the curve is $(-4, -11)$.

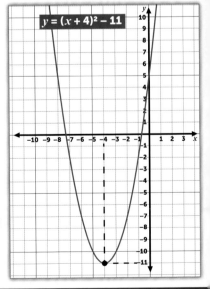

$y = (x + 4)^2 - 11$

Calculating the nth Term

In a number sequence, n is used to represent the position of each item (known as a term).

1st term $n = 1$	2nd term $n = 2$	3rd term $n = 3$	4th term $n = 4$
3	6	9	12

+3   +3   +3

The rule for this sequence is:

$$+3 \times n \text{ or } +3n$$

$+3 \times 1 = 3$ $+3 \times 2 = 6$

$+3 \times 3 = 9$ $+3 \times 4 = 12$

To find the nth term rule of a linear sequence, follow the steps outlined below:

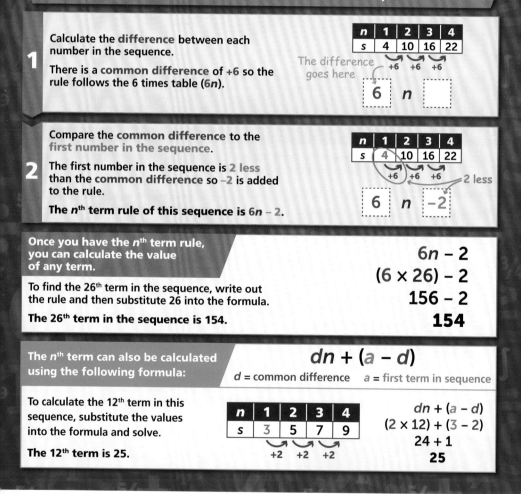

1

Calculate the **difference** between each number in the sequence.

There is a **common difference** of +6 so the rule follows the 6 times table (**6n**).

n	1	2	3	4
s	4	10	16	22

+6   +6   +6

The difference goes here

| 6 | n | |

2

Compare the **common difference** to the first number in the sequence.

The first number in the sequence is **2 less** than the **common difference** so −2 is added to the rule.

The nth term rule of this sequence is **6n − 2**.

n	1	2	3	4
s	4	10	16	22

+6   +6   +6   2 less

| 6 | n | −2 |

Once you have the nth term rule, you can calculate the value of any term.

To find the 26th term in the sequence, write out the rule and then substitute 26 into the formula.

The 26th term in the sequence is 154.

$$6n - 2$$
$$(6 \times 26) - 2$$
$$156 - 2$$
$$\mathbf{154}$$

The nth term can also be calculated using the following formula:

$$dn + (a - d)$$

d = common difference a = first term in sequence

To calculate the 12th term in this sequence, substitute the values into the formula and solve.

The 12th term is 25.

n	1	2	3	4
s	3	5	7	9

+2   +2   +2

$$dn + (a - d)$$
$$(2 \times 12) + (3 - 2)$$
$$24 + 1$$
$$\mathbf{25}$$

daydream EDUCATION

To find the nth term rule of a quadratic sequence, follow the steps below:

Example 1

1 Calculate the **difference between each number in the sequence.**

The difference between each number is changing so work out the **second difference** - the difference of the differences.

n	1	2	3	4	5
s	1	10	25	46	73

+9 +15 +21 +27

+6 +6 +6

2 Divide this value by 2 to determine the **coefficient of the n^2 term.**

$$6 \div 2 = 3$$

$$\boxed{3}\; n^2 \;\boxed{+bn+c}$$

3 Work out the sequence of numbers in $3n^2$ and then subtract these from each number in the original sequence (s).

All answers are the same (–2). This tells us that the nth term rule does not contain a bn term.

Therefore, the nth term rule is $3n^2 - 2$.

n	1	2	3	4	5
s	1	10	25	46	73
$3n^2$	3	12	27	48	75
$s - 3n^2$	-2	-2	-2	-2	-2

$$3n^2 - 2$$

Example 2

1 Calculate the **difference between each number in the sequence.**

The difference between each number is changing so work out the **second difference** - the difference of the differences.

n	1	2	3	4	5
s	3	9	17	27	39

+6 +8 +10 +12

+2 +2 +2

2 Divide this value by 2 to determine the **coefficient of the n^2 term.**

Because $1n^2 = n^2$, there is no need to write 1 in front of n^2.

$$2 \div 2 = 1$$

$$\boxed{}\; n^2 \;\boxed{+bn+c}$$

3 Work out the sequence of numbers in n^2 and then subtract these from each number in the original sequence (s).

The **answers form a linear sequence.** This tells us that the formula for the sequence is of the form $ax^2 + bn + c$.

n	1	2	3	4	5
s	3	9	17	27	39
n^2	1	4	9	16	25
$s - n^2$	2	5	8	11	14

4 To identify the **value of b,** find the nth term rule of the new linear sequence by calculating the **difference between each number in the sequence.**

There is a common difference of +3, so the value of b is 3.

s	2	5	8	11	14

+3 +3 +3 +3

$$n^2 \;\boxed{+\,3}\,n+\;\boxed{c}$$

5 To find the **value of c,** compare the **common difference** to the **first number in the sequence.** The first number in the sequence is 1 less than the common difference, so the value of c is –1.

Therefore, the nth term rule is $n^2 + 3n - 1$.

s	2	5	8	11	14

+3 +3 +3 +3

1 less

$$n^2 \;\boxed{+\,3}\,n \;\boxed{-\,1}$$

Inequalities

< Less than

$x < 3$ means that
x is less than 3

> Greater than

$x > 7$ means that
x is greater than 7

≤ Less than or equal to

$y \leq 3$ means that
y is less than or equal to 3

≥ Greater than or equal to

$y \geq 7$ means that
y is greater than or equal to 7

Number Lines

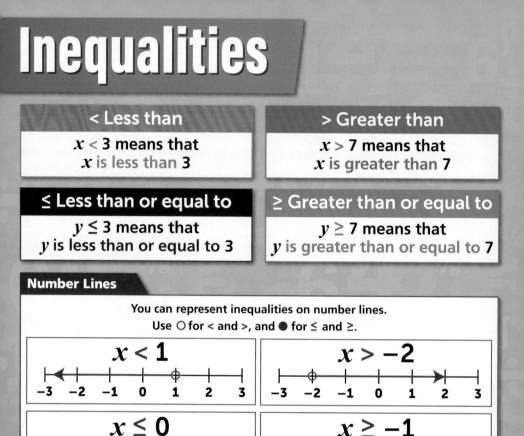

You can represent inequalities on number lines.
Use ○ for < and >, and ● for ≤ and ≥.

$x < 1$

| −3 | −2 | −1 | 0 | 1 | 2 | 3 |

$x > -2$

| −3 | −2 | −1 | 0 | 1 | 2 | 3 |

$x \leq 0$

| −4 | −3 | −2 | −1 | 0 | 1 | 2 |

$x \geq -1$

| −2 | −1 | 0 | 1 | 2 | 3 | 4 |

Solving Inequalities

Most equations involving inequalities are solved in the same way as standard equations. However, when multiplying or dividing by a negative number, you must reverse the inequality.

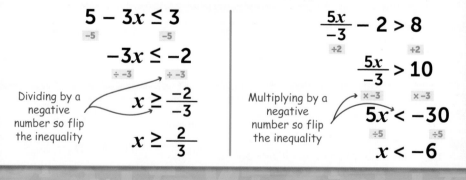

$$5 - 3x \leq 3$$
$$-5 \qquad -5$$
$$-3x \leq -2$$
$$\div -3 \qquad \div -3$$

Dividing by a negative number so flip the inequality

$$x \geq \frac{-2}{-3}$$
$$x \geq \frac{2}{3}$$

$$\frac{5x}{-3} - 2 > 8$$
$$+2 \qquad +2$$
$$\frac{5x}{-3} > 10$$

Multiplying by a negative number so flip the inequality

$$\times -3 \qquad \times -3$$
$$5x < -30$$
$$\div 5 \qquad \div 5$$
$$x < -6$$

daydream
EDUCATION

Graphing Inequalities

Follow the steps outlined below when graphing inequalities.

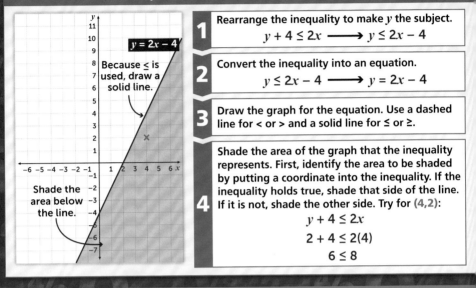

Because ≤ is used, draw a solid line.

$y = 2x - 4$

Shade the area below the line.

1 Rearrange the inequality to make y the subject.
$$y + 4 \leq 2x \longrightarrow y \leq 2x - 4$$

2 Convert the inequality into an equation.
$$y \leq 2x - 4 \longrightarrow y = 2x - 4$$

3 Draw the graph for the equation. Use a dashed line for < or > and a solid line for ≤ or ≥.

4 Shade the area of the graph that the inequality represents. First, identify the area to be shaded by putting a coordinate into the inequality. If the inequality holds true, shade that side of the line. If it is not, shade the other side. Try for (4,2):
$$y + 4 \leq 2x$$
$$2 + 4 \leq 2(4)$$
$$6 \leq 8$$

You will often be asked to find a region that satisfies various inequalities.

Shade the region that satisfies all the following inequalities:
$$\frac{y-1}{2} < x \qquad y > 1 \qquad y - 5 \leq -x$$

$y = -x + 5$

$y = 2x + 1$

$y = 1$

1 Rearrange the inequalities to make y the subject.
$$\frac{y-1}{2} < x \longrightarrow y < 2x + 1$$
$$y > 1 \longrightarrow y > 1$$
$$y - 5 \leq -x \longrightarrow y \leq -x + 5$$

2 Convert the inequalities into equations.
$$y < 2x + 1 \longrightarrow y = 2x + 1$$
$$y > 1 \longrightarrow y = 1$$
$$y \leq -x + 5 \longrightarrow y = -x + 5$$

3 Draw the graphs for the equations. Use a dashed line for < or > and a solid line for ≤ or ≥.

4 Shade the area of the graph that satisfies all the criteria specified. Test a coordinate to ensure it is true for all the inequalities. Try for (2,2):
$y < 2x + 1$	$y > 1$	$y \leq -x + 5$
$2 < 2(2) + 1$	$2 > 1$	$2 \leq -2 + 5$
$2 < 5$		$2 \leq 3$

Simultaneous Equations

To solve simultaneous equations, eliminate one of the variables to find the value of the other variable. The value of the eliminated variable can then be found.

To solve these simultaneous equations, follow the steps outlined below.

$$2x = 7 + 3y$$
$$5x + y = -8$$

1 Rearrange the equations into the form $ax + by = c$ and label them **1** and **2**.

$$2x = 7 + 3y$$
$$\quad -3y \qquad -3y$$
❶ $2x - 3y = 7$ | **❷** $5x + y = -8$

2 If the coefficients of a variable are the same in both equations, elimination can be performed through addition or subtraction. However, in these equations, the coefficients differ, so multiply one or both equations to make the coefficients of one variable the same. The y-coefficients in these equations can be made the same by multiplying equation 2 by 3.

❶ $2x - 3y = 7$ | **❷** $5x + y = -8$
$3(5x + y = -8)$
$15x + 3y = -24$

3 The y-terms now have the same coefficient. Because they have opposite signs, the equations need to be added together. If they had the same sign, one of the equations would need to be subtracted from the other.

STOP (Same = Takeaway, Opposite = Plus)

❶ $\quad 2x - 3y = 7$
❷ $+ 15x + 3y = -24$
$\overline{\qquad 17x = -17}$

4 Solve the equation.

$$17x = -17$$
$$\quad \div 17 \qquad \div 17$$
$$x = -1$$

5 Now that the value of one variable (x) is known, you can find the value of the other variable (y) by substituting the first variable (x) into one of the original equations (**1** or **2**) and solving.

❶ $2x - 3y = 7$
$2(-1) - 3y = 7$
$-2 - 3y = 7$
$\quad +2 \qquad +2$
$-3y = 9$
$\quad \div -3 \quad \div -3$
$y = -3$

6 The equation is now solved. To check your answer, substitute the values into the other equation and solve.

$$5x + y = -8$$
$$5(-1) + (-3) = -8$$
$$-5 + -3 = -8$$

daydream EDUCATION

Graphing Simultaneous Equations

Simultaneous equations can be solved by drawing the graphs of the equations. The solution can be found at the point(s) where the two lines intersect.

$$2x - y = 4$$
$$y = x - 1$$

Make a table of values for both equations. Find y when $x = 0$ and x when $y = 0$, and choose at least one other point.

$2x - y = 4$

x	0	2	4
y	-4	0	4

$y = x - 1$

x	0	2	4
y	-1	1	3

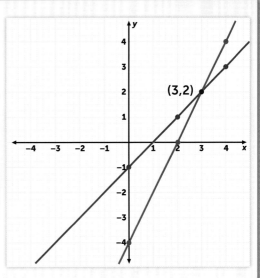

Plot the points and list where the lines intersect. The point of intersection is (3,2). Therefore, $x = 3$ and $y = 2$.

When simultaneous equations involve a linear equation and a quadratic equation, the solution(s) can be found where the two equations intersect.

$$y - 2x = 1$$
$$y = x^2 - 2$$

Make a table of values for both equations.

$y - 2x = 1$

x	-1	0	2
y	-1	1	5

$y = x^2 - 2$

x	-1	0	2
y	-1	-2	2

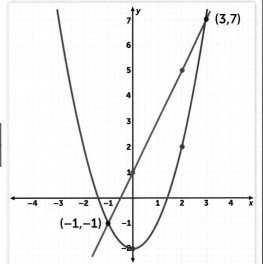

Plot the points and list where the lines intersect.

The graphs intersect at (-1,-1) and (3,7). Therefore, $x = -1$, $y = -1$ and $x = 3$, $y = 7$.

Iterative Method

Trial and Improvement

Trial and improvement can be used to find solutions to equations.

Solve $x^3 + 7x - 2 = 55$ to 1 decimal place (d.p.).

x	$x^3 + 7x - 2 =$	$= 55$?
3	$3^3 + 7(3) - 2 = 46$	Too small
4	$4^3 + 7(4) - 2 = 90$	Too big
3.5	$3.5^3 + 7(3.5) - 2 = 65.375$	Too big
3.4	$3.4^3 + 7(3.4) - 2 = 61.104$	Too big
3.3	$3.3^3 + 7(3.3) - 2 = 57.037$	Too big
3.2	$3.2^3 + 7(3.2) - 2 = 53.168$	Too small

Check the midpoint of 3.2 and 3.3 to determine which value is closest:

$3.25^3 + 7(3.25) - 2 = \mathbf{55.078125}$

This is too big so the solution to 1 d.p. is 3.2.

1 Choose an integer value for x and solve.

2 If the answer is too small, try a bigger integer. If the answer is too big, try a smaller integer.

3 Once you have two consecutive integers – one on each side of the solution – try the midpoint between these values. If the value is too high, try a lower one. If the value is too low, try a higher one.

4 Once you have the two nearest values to 1 d.p., check the midpoint of these values to determine the solution.

Flow Charts

You can also use the flow chart below to find the solution to a problem.

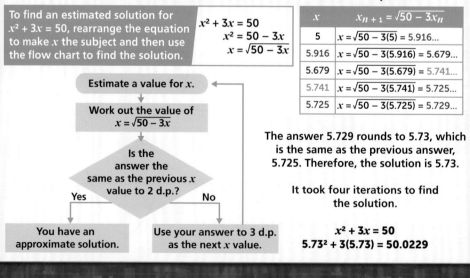

To find an estimated solution for $x^2 + 3x = 50$, rearrange the equation to make x the subject and then use the flow chart to find the solution.

$x^2 + 3x = 50$
$x^2 = 50 - 3x$
$x = \sqrt{50 - 3x}$

x	$x_{n+1} = \sqrt{50 - 3x_n}$
5	$x = \sqrt{50 - 3(5)} = 5.916...$
5.916	$x = \sqrt{50 - 3(5.916)} = 5.679...$
5.679	$x = \sqrt{50 - 3(5.679)} = 5.741...$
5.741	$x = \sqrt{50 - 3(5.741)} = 5.725...$
5.725	$x = \sqrt{50 - 3(5.725)} = 5.729...$

Estimate a value for x.

Work out the value of $x = \sqrt{50 - 3x}$

Is the answer the same as the previous x value to 2 d.p.?

Yes → You have an approximate solution.

No → Use your answer to 3 d.p. as the next x value.

The answer 5.729 rounds to 5.73, which is the same as the previous answer, 5.725. Therefore, the solution is 5.73.

It took four iterations to find the solution.

$x^2 + 3x = 50$
$5.73^2 + 3(5.73) = 50.0229$

daydream
EDUCATION

Iterative Notation

A number sequence can be represented algebraically, with the $(n + 1)^{th}$ term written as a formula in terms of the previous term.

Sequence	Term-to-Term Rule	Notation
1, 2, 4, 8, ...	Double the previous term, starting with 1.	$u_{n+1} = 2u_n$ where $u_1 = 1$
200, 100, 50, 25, ...	Halve the previous term, starting with 200.	$u_{n+1} = \frac{u_n}{2}$ where $u_1 = 200$

The formula can be used to work out subsequent terms in the sequence.

A sequence is defined by the term-to-term rule:
Given that $u_1 = -1$, find u_2 and u_3.

$$u_{n+1} = \frac{(u_n)^3 - 3}{8}$$

1 To find u_2 substitute the value of u_1 into the formula and solve.

$$u_2 = \frac{(-1)^3 - 3}{8} = \frac{-4}{8} = -0.5$$

2 To find u_3 substitute the value of u_2 into the formula and solve.

$$u_3 = \frac{(-0.5)^3 - 3}{8} = \frac{-3.125}{8} = -0.390625$$

Iterative Formulae

Iterative formulae can also be used to solve equations. The equation is rearranged into an iterative formula, which is then repeatedly used to get closer and closer to the solution.

Original Equation	Reformatted Equation	Iterative Formula
$x^2 - 4x - 7 = 0$	$x = \sqrt{4x + 7}$	$u_{n+1} = \sqrt{4u_n + 7}$

Equations can often be rearranged into several different iterative formulae.

Aroon is trying to solve $5x^2 - 3x - 4 = 0$ by using the iterative formula. Solve to 2 d.p. starting with an initial value of $u_1 = 5$.

$$u_{n+1} = \sqrt{\frac{3u_n + 4}{5}}$$

Use the iterative formula to find the value of u_2, given that $u_1 = 5$.

Repeat this for each answer until the final condition is met.

You can use the **Ans** button on a calculator so you do not have to keep entering the calculations. Simply press 5 and = to set the last answer in your calculator as 5. Then set up the formula as $\sqrt{\frac{3ans + 4}{5}}$, and keep pressing = for the next iterations.

The last two values both round to 1.24 to 2 d.p. so one solution is 1.24.

Value of u_n	$u_{n+1} = \sqrt{\frac{3u_n + 4}{5}}$
5	$u_2 = \sqrt{\frac{3(5) + 4}{5}} = 1.949358869$
1.949358869	$u_3 = \sqrt{\frac{3(1.949358869) + 4}{5}} = 1.403429842$
1.403429842	$u_4 = \sqrt{\frac{3(1.403429842) + 4}{5}} = 1.281428073$
1.281428073	$u_5 = \sqrt{\frac{3(1.281428073) + 4}{5}} = 1.252540156$
1.252540156	$u_6 = \sqrt{\frac{3(1.252540156) + 4}{5}} = 1.2456019$
1.2456019	$u_7 = \sqrt{\frac{3(1.2456019) + 4}{5}} = 1.243929717$
1.243929717	$u_8 = \sqrt{\frac{3(1.243929717) + 4}{5}} = 1.243526369$
1.243526369	

Functions

A function relates an input to an output. It takes an input, processes it and outputs a value.

A function is often represented as $f(x)$, with f being the function name and x being the input. $f(x) = x^2$ tells us that the function of x equals x squared. So if x is input, x^2 is output.

When x is a number, you can calculate the output.

Note: Functions are not always written in the form f(x), any letters can be used. ⟶

Input	Function		Output
8	$f(x) = x^2$	$f(8) = 8^2$	64
4	$f(x) = 1 - x + x^2$	$f(4) = 1 - 4 + 4^2$	13
3	$s(t) = \frac{2t + 4}{t}$	$s(3) = \frac{2(3) + 4}{3}$	$\frac{10}{3}$

Composite Functions

A composite function contains two functions combined in a single function; $fg(x)$. One function is applied to the result of the other function. Always do the function closest to x first.

$$fg(x)$$

Function g
$g(x) = x - 2$ ⟶ Function f
$f(x) = x^2 + 5$

To find $fg(x)$ of the above:	To find $fg(4)$ of the above:	To find $gf(4)$ of the above:
Rewrite $fg(x)$ as $f(g(x))$.	Rewrite $fg(4)$ as $f(g(4))$.	Rewrite $gf(4)$ as $g(f(4))$.
Replace $g(x)$ with the expression it represents: $f(x - 2)$.	Replace $g(4)$ with the expression it represents: $f(4 - 2)$. This can be simplified to $f(2)$.	Replace $f(4)$ with the expression it represents: $g(4^2 + 5)$. This can be simplified to $g(21)$.
Place this into f and simplify: $f(x - 2) = (x - 2)^2 + 5$ $fg(x) = x^2 - 4x + 9$	Place this into f and solve: $f(2) = (2)^2 + 5$ $= 4 + 5$ $fg(4) = 9$	Place this into g and solve: $g(21) = 21 - 2$ $gf(4) = 19$

As can be seen above, $fg(x)$ does not always equal $gf(x)$.

Inverse Functions

An inverse function $f^{-1}(x)$ reverses an original function $f(x)$. Flow diagrams can help you determine inverse functions of functions where x appears once. Simply reverse the operations in the original function to find the inverse function.

Find $f^{-1}(x)$ where $f(x) = 4x - 10$.

$$x \xrightarrow{} \boxed{\times 4} \xrightarrow{4x} \boxed{-10} \xrightarrow{} 4x - 10$$

$$\frac{x + 10}{4} \xleftarrow{} \boxed{\div 4} \xleftarrow{x + 10} \boxed{+10} \xleftarrow{} x$$

Where x appears more than once, follow the steps outlined below.

	Rewrite as $x = f(y)$.	Make y the subject.	Change y to $f^{-1}(x)$.
Find $f^{-1}(x)$ if $f(x) = \frac{3x + 2}{x}$	$f(x) = \frac{3x + 2}{x}$ $x = \frac{3y + 2}{y}$	$yx = 3y + 2$ $yx - 3y = 2$ $y(x - 3) = 2$ $y = \frac{2}{x - 3}$	$y = \frac{2}{x - 3}$ $f^{-1}(x) = \frac{2}{x - 3}$

daydream EDUCATION

Straight Line Graphs

Vertical and Horizontal Lines

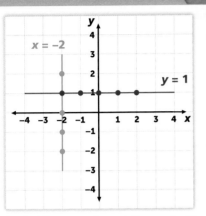

Vertical lines pass through the x-axis. All points on a vertical line have the same x-coordinate.

x = -2	(-2,-2)	(-2,-1)	(-2,0)	(-2,1)	(-2,2)

Horizontal lines pass through the y-axis. All points on a horizontal line have the same y-coordinate.

y = 1	(-2,1)	(-1,1)	(0,1)	(1,1)	(2,1)

Diagonal Lines

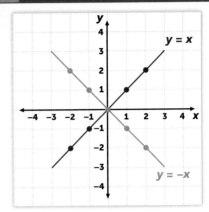

$y = x$ is diagonal and slopes upward from left to right.

x	-2	-1	0	1	2
y	-2	-1	0	1	2

$y = -x$ is diagonal and slopes downward from left to right.

x	-2	-1	0	1	2
y	2	1	0	-1	-2

Straight Line Equation

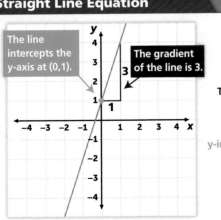

The line intercepts the y-axis at (0,1).

The gradient of the line is 3.

The standard equation of a straight line is:

$$y = mx + c$$

m = gradient of line c = y-intercept

The gradient can be calculated using the formula:

$$\text{gradient } (m) = \frac{\text{change in } y}{\text{change in } x}$$

y-intercept = where the line passes through the y-axis

The equation of the straight line is: $y = 3x + 1$

$$\text{gradient } (m) = \frac{\text{change in } y}{\text{change in } x} = \frac{3}{1} = 3$$

y-intercept = (0,1)

Drawing Straight Line Graphs

How to Draw Straight Line Graphs

To draw a straight line graph, you need to plot three points: two points to draw the line and one point to check if the line is correct.

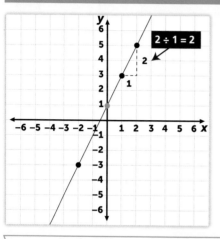

Draw the graph of $y = 2x + 1$

To identify which points to plot, work out the value of y for three different *values of x.*

$x =$	−2	1	2
$2x$	−4	2	4
$+1$	−3	3	5
$y =$	−3	3	5

Plot the three points:

(−2,−3)   **(1,3)**   **(2,5)**

If the plotted points do not form a straight line, there is an error.
You can also check if the **y-intercept** and **gradient** are correct on the graph.

How to Draw Straight Line Graphs Without a Table of Values

A table of values is not always needed to plot the graph of a straight line.

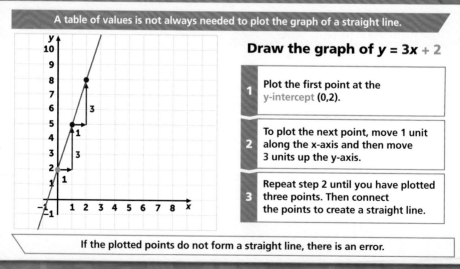

Draw the graph of $y = 3x + 2$

1 Plot the first point at the y-intercept **(0,2)**.

2 To plot the next point, move 1 unit along the x-axis and then move 3 units up the y-axis.

3 Repeat step 2 until you have plotted three points. Then connect the points to create a straight line.

If the plotted points do not form a straight line, there is an error.

daydream EDUCATION

Finding the Equation of a Straight Line

Finding the Equation of a Straight Line

To find the equation of a straight line, follow the steps outlined below:

1 Find the y-intercept of the graph. This is the value of c. The line intercepts the y-axis at $(0,1)$ so $c = +1$.

2 Pick two coordinates on the line, and use the following formula to calculate the gradient (m):

$$m = \frac{\text{change in } y}{\text{change in } x}$$

$$= \frac{-1 - -3}{1 - 2}$$

$$= \frac{2}{-1}$$

$$m = -2$$

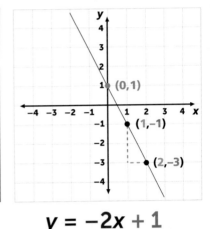

The gradient (m) is –2 and the intercept (c) is +1. Therefore, the equation of the line is:

$$y = -2x + 1$$

Finding the Equation of a Line Through Two Points

To find the equation of a straight line that passes through two points, follow the steps outlined below:

Find the equation of the straight line that passes through (8,6) and (2,3).

1 Find the gradient (m).

$$m = \frac{\text{change in } y}{\text{change in } x}$$

$$= \frac{6 - 3}{8 - 2}$$

$$= \frac{3}{6}$$

$$m = 0.5$$

2 Substitute one of the coordinates and the gradient (0.5) into the equation $y = mx + c$, and solve to find the value of c:

$$y = mx + c$$
$$6 = 0.5 \times 8 + c$$
$$6 = 4 + c$$
$$-4 \quad -4$$
$$2 = c$$

3 Substitute the values of c (2) and m (0.5) into the equation $y = mx + c$.

$$y = 0.5x + 2$$

Parallel & Perpendicular Lines

Parallel Lines

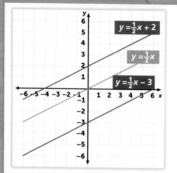

Graphs that have the same gradient (value of m), are parallel and will never meet.

Graphs that pass through the origin are of the form $y = mx$ (e.g. $y = \frac{1}{2}x$). They do not contain a y-intercept (value for c).

Graphs with a positive gradient (e.g. $y = 2x + 1$) slope upward from left to right.

Graphs with a negative gradient (e.g. $y = -2x + 1$) slope downward from left to right.

Perpendicular Lines

Two lines that cross at a right angle are perpendicular. The product of the two perpendicular lines' gradients is –1. (Not true for vertical and horizontal perpendicular lines.)

$$m_1 \times m_2 = -1$$

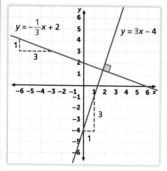

This graph shows perpendicular lines with gradients of 3 and $-\frac{1}{3}$.

$$3 \times -\frac{1}{3} = -1$$

This table displays pairs of perpendicular gradients.

m_1 (original gradient)	1	2	–4	$\frac{1}{5}$	3
m_2 (perpendicular gradient)	–1	$-\frac{1}{2}$	$\frac{1}{4}$	–5	$-\frac{1}{3}$

To find the gradient of a perpendicular line, its negative reciprocal is required:

$$m_2 = -\frac{1}{m_1}$$

For fractions, turn them upside down and change the sign.

Finding the Equation of a Perpendicular Line

Find the equation of the line that is perpendicular to $y = 2x + 3$ through point (1,–1.5).

1 Identify the gradient (m) of the line $y = 2x + 3$.	**2** Find the gradient of the perpendicular line. Place this into the form $y = mx + c$.	**3** The line passes through (1,–1.5), so substitute this into the equation to find c. $x = 1$ and $y = -1.5$	**4** Write out the full equation for the line that is perpendicular to line $y = 2x + 3$.
$y = mx + c$ $y = 2x + 3$ $m = 2$	$m_2 = -\dfrac{1}{m_1}$ $m_2 = -\dfrac{1}{2}$ $y = -\dfrac{1}{2}x + c$	$y = -0.5x + c$ $-1.5 = -0.5(1) + c$ $-1.5 = -0.5 + c$ $-1 = c$	$y = -\dfrac{1}{2}x + -1$ $y = -\dfrac{1}{2}x - 1$

daydream
EDUCATION

Quadratic Graphs

Graphs of quadratic functions contain a squared term, x^2, and are parabolas, or U-shaped. If a is negative, the parabola will be upside down.

The standard form of a quadratic function is:

$$y = ax^2 + bx + c$$

Solving Quadratic Equations Graphically

Solve $y = x^2 - 4x + 3$ when $y = 0$.

1. Make a table of values. Substitute x-values into the equation to find the y-values.

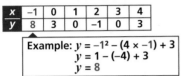

x	−1	0	1	2	3	4
y	8	3	0	−1	0	3

Example: $y = -1^2 - (4 \times -1) + 3$
$y = 1 - (-4) + 3$
$y = 8$

2. Plot each point on the graph, and join them up with a smooth curve. If one point does not naturally fit on the curve, it is wrong.

3. The solution to the equation can be found where the graph crosses the x-axis.

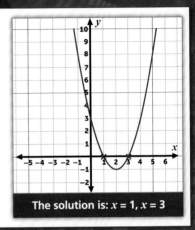

The solution is: $x = 1$, $x = 3$

Sketching Quadratics

You can solve quadratic equations and use the solution to sketch the graph.

To sketch the graph of $x^2 - 4x - 5 = 0$, firstly solve the equation:

$$x^2 - 4x - 5 = 0$$
$$(x + 1)(x - 5) = 0$$
$$x = -1, x = 5$$

The solution shows that where $y = 0$, $x = -1$, $x = 5$. Therefore, the x-intercepts are (−1,0) and (5,0).

As a quadratic is symmetrical, the x-coordinate of the turning point is halfway between −1 and 5. Therefore, the x-coordinate of the turning point is 2.

If you substitute 2 into the equation and solve, you can find the y-coordinate of the turning point.

$y = x^2 - 4x - 5$
$y = 2^2 - (4 \times 2) - 5$
$y = -9$

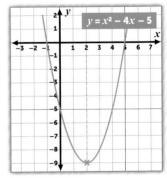

The y-coordinate of the turning point is −9 so the coordinate of the turning point is (2,−9).

By using the x-intercepts and turning point, you should be able to sketch the graph.

daydream
EDUCATION

55

Standard Graphs

The ability to recognise, sketch and interpret the following graphs is a vital element of mathematics.

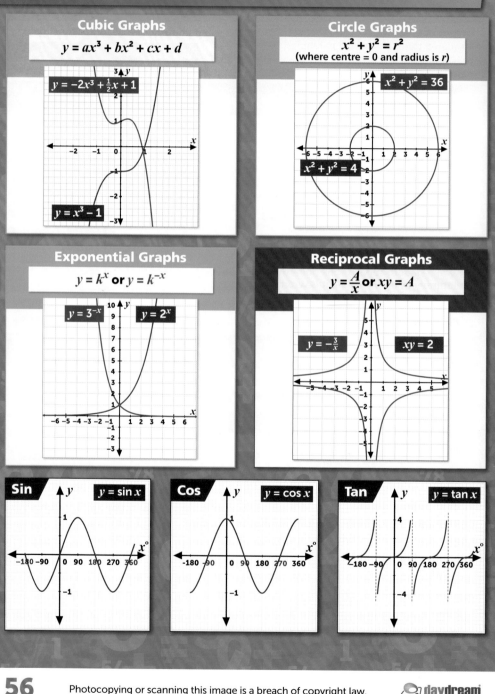

Cubic Graphs

$$y = ax^3 + bx^2 + cx + d$$

$y = -2x^3 + \frac{1}{2}x + 1$

$y = x^3 - 1$

Circle Graphs

$$x^2 + y^2 = r^2$$
(where centre = 0 and radius is r)

$x^2 + y^2 = 36$

$x^2 + y^2 = 4$

Exponential Graphs

$$y = k^x \text{ or } y = k^{-x}$$

$y = 3^{-x}$ $y = 2^x$

Reciprocal Graphs

$$y = \frac{A}{x} \text{ or } xy = A$$

$y = -\frac{3}{x}$ $xy = 2$

Sin
$y = \sin x$

Cos
$y = \cos x$

Tan
$y = \tan x$

daydream
EDUCATION

Transformation of Graphs

It is important to understand the relationship between changes to the algebraic form of a curve and the effect on the graph of the curve.

If y = an expression involving x, then we can write $y = f(x)$.
In the following examples it is important to remember that k is a constant.

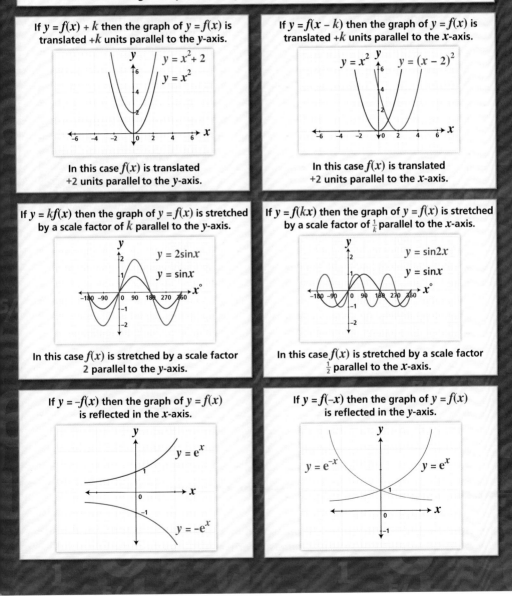

If $y = f(x) + k$ then the graph of $y = f(x)$ is translated $+k$ units parallel to the y-axis.

$y = x^2 + 2$
$y = x^2$

In this case $f(x)$ is translated +2 units parallel to the y-axis.

If $y = f(x - k)$ then the graph of $y = f(x)$ is translated $+k$ units parallel to the x-axis.

$y = x^2$
$y = (x - 2)^2$

In this case $f(x)$ is translated +2 units parallel to the x-axis.

If $y = kf(x)$ then the graph of $y = f(x)$ is stretched by a scale factor of k parallel to the y-axis.

$y = 2\sin x$
$y = \sin x$

In this case $f(x)$ is stretched by a scale factor 2 parallel to the y-axis.

If $y = f(kx)$ then the graph of $y = f(x)$ is stretched by a scale factor of $\frac{1}{k}$ parallel to the x-axis.

$y = \sin 2x$
$y = \sin x$

In this case $f(x)$ is stretched by a scale factor $\frac{1}{2}$ parallel to the x-axis.

If $y = -f(x)$ then the graph of $y = f(x)$ is reflected in the x-axis.

$y = e^x$
$y = -e^x$

If $y = f(-x)$ then the graph of $y = f(x)$ is reflected in the y-axis.

$y = e^{-x}$
$y = e^x$

Distance-Time Graphs

A distance-time graph is a type of travel graph. Distance is measured up the *y*-axis (vertical) and time is measured along the *x*-axis (horizontal).

Gradient of graph = Speed
The steeper the graph, the faster the speed.

$$\text{Speed} = \frac{\text{Distance}}{\text{Time}}$$

Sections of the graph that slope **upward** from left to right represent distance travelled away from the starting point.

Sections of the graph that slope **downward** from left to right represent distance travelled toward the starting point.

A horizontal line indicates that no distance is being travelled.

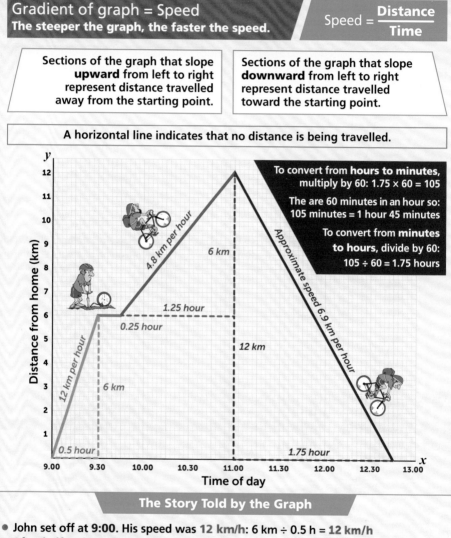

To convert from **hours to minutes**, multiply by 60: 1.75 × 60 = 105

The are 60 minutes in an hour so: 105 minutes = 1 hour 45 minutes

To convert from **minutes to hours**, divide by 60: 105 ÷ 60 = 1.75 hours

Distance from home (km) — *y*

12 km per hour

4.8 km per hour

6 km

Approximate speed 6.9 km per hour

0.25 hour

1.25 hour

6 km

12 km

0.5 hour

1.75 hour

Time of day — *x*

9.00 9.30 10.00 10.30 11.00 11.30 12.00 12.30 13.00

The Story Told by the Graph

- John set off at **9:00**. His speed was **12 km/h**: 6 km ÷ 0.5 h = **12 km/h**
- After half an hour, he had a puncture. It took **15 minutes** to repair.
- He continued his journey at a slower speed of **4.8 km/h**: 6 km ÷ 1.25 h = **4.8 km/h**
- At **11:00** he started his journey home and arrived at **12:45**. His speed was **6.9 km/h**: 12 km ÷ 1.75 h = **6.9 km/h**

daydream EDUCATION

Velocity-Time Graphs

In velocity-time graphs, velocity is measured along the y-axis, and time is measured along the x-axis.

Acceleration

Acceleration is the rate at which an object changes its velocity.

Acceleration = $\dfrac{\text{Change in velocity}}{\text{Change in time}}$ Measured in metres per second squared (m/s²)

Gradient of graph = Acceleration
The steeper the gradient, the greater the acceleration or deceleration is.

The graph shows the velocity of a skydiver as a function of time.

Sections of a graph that slope upward from left to right have a positive gradient and represent acceleration.

Sections of the graph that slope downward from left to right have a negative gradient and represent deceleration.

Horizontal line = Constant velocity

Area under graph = Total distance travelled

After 10 s, the diver reaches his terminal velocity so his velocity remains constant.

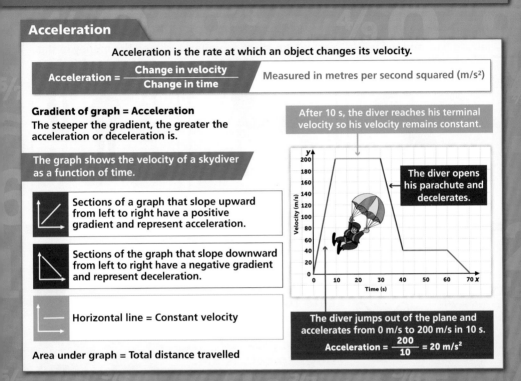

The diver opens his parachute and decelerates.

The diver jumps out of the plane and accelerates from 0 m/s to 200 m/s in 10 s.
Acceleration = $\dfrac{200}{10}$ = 20 m/s²

Area Under a Graph

When a velocity-time graph is made up of straight lines, the total distance travelled can be calculated by splitting the area into shapes, working out their areas and adding them together.

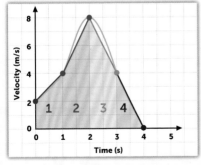

When a graph has curved lines, the total distance travelled is estimated by roughly splitting the area up into trapeziums and adding their areas together.

Area 1:   ½ × (2 + 4) × 1 = 3
Area 2:   ½ × (4 + 8) × 1 = 6
Area 3:   ½ × (8 + 4) × 1 = 6
Area 4:   ½ × (4 + 0) × 1 = 2

Total: = 17

The total distance travelled is 17 m.

The total area under the curved line is likely to be an underestimate as the combined size of the trapeziums is smaller than the actual size of the area under the line.

Ratios

A ratio is a way of comparing two or more quantities.

Purple paint is made by mixing blue and red paint in the ratio of 2 to 3.

To make mortar, sand and cement are mixed together in the ratio of 5 to 2.

Lilly, Jack and Jo have shared the money in the ratio of 2 to 6 to 3.

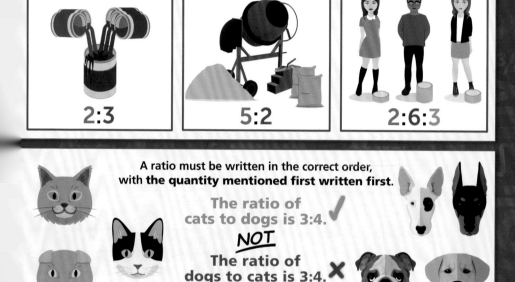

2:3

5:2

2:6:3

A ratio must be written in the correct order, with **the quantity mentioned first written first**.

The ratio of cats to dogs is 3:4. ✓

NOT

The ratio of dogs to cats is 3:4. ✗

Note that the ratio of dogs to cats is **4:3**.

Ratios are easier to work out when they are in their simplest form.
To simplify ratios, both numbers must be **divided by their highest common factor**.

The ratio of blue to red tiles is 6 to 3 but this can be simplified.

3 is the highest common factor of 6 and 3, so divide both numbers by 3.

6:3

÷3   ÷3

2:1

Can you simplify these ratios to their simplest form?	**6:4**	**9:3**	**2:8:4**

daydream
EDUCATION

Dividing in a Ratio

Sometimes an amount needs to be divided according to a particular ratio.

Ava, Isla and Freya made **£315** selling balloons at a fayre. They agreed to split the money in the ratio of **3:2:4**. How much money does each person get?

1 Add the numbers in the ratio to calculate the total number of parts.

$$3 + 2 + 4 = 9$$

2 Find the value of 1 part by dividing the total amount by the total number of parts, 9.

$$315 \div 9 = 35$$
1 part = **35**

3 Multiply the value of 1 part, **35**, by the numbers in the ratio to calculate how much money each person gets.

$$3 \times 35 = 105$$
$$2 \times 35 = 70$$
$$4 \times 35 = 140$$

4 **315** divided in the ratio of **3:2:4** is **105:70:140**. Check your answer by adding together the values.

Ava	Isla	Freya
£105	£70	£140

$$105 + 70 + 140 = 315$$

If you know the value of one part of a ratio, you can calculate the values of the other parts, and the total sum of the ratio.

To make turquoise paint, blue paint and green paint are mixed in the ratio of **4:7**. If Eva has **2.4 litres of blue paint**, how much green paint does she need and how much turquoise paint can she make?

1 Calculate the value of 1 part by dividing the amount of blue paint by the number of blue parts in the ratio.

$$2.4 \div 4 = 0.6$$
1 part = 0.6

2 To calculate the amount of green paint that is needed, multiply the value of 1 part by the number of green parts in the ratio.

$$0.6 \times 7 = 4.2$$
Eva needs 4.2 litres of green paint.

3 To calculate the amount of turquoise paint that Eva can make, multiply the value of 1 part by the total number of parts in the ratio.

$$0.6 \times 11 = 6.6$$
Eva can make 6.6 litres of turquoise paint.

Scale

0   50cm

Scale 1:50

The plan of Oliver's bedroom is drawn at a scale of **1:50**. This means that the bedroom is 50 times bigger in real life than in the drawing.

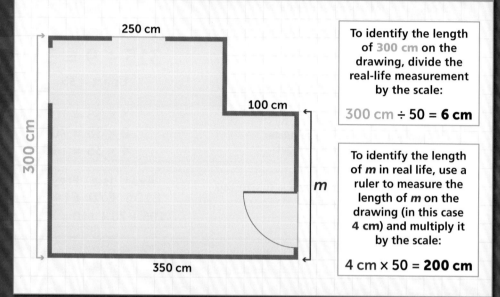

250 cm

100 cm

300 cm

m

350 cm

To identify the length of **300 cm** on the drawing, divide the real-life measurement by the scale:

$300 \text{ cm} \div 50 = \textbf{6 cm}$

To identify the length of **m** in real life, use a ruler to measure the length of **m** on the drawing (in this case 4 cm) and multiply it by the scale:

$4 \text{ cm} \times 50 = \textbf{200 cm}$

Using Scales to Draw and Read Maps

The map below has a scale of **1:50,000**.
This means the map is 50,000 times smaller than the actual area shown.

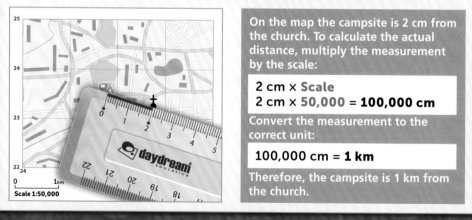

0   1km

Scale 1:50,000

On the map the campsite is 2 cm from the church. To calculate the actual distance, multiply the measurement by the scale:

2 cm × Scale
$2 \text{ cm} \times 50,000 = \textbf{100,000 cm}$

Convert the measurement to the correct unit:

$100,000 \text{ cm} = \textbf{1 km}$

Therefore, the campsite is 1 km from the church.

daydream EDUCATION

Direct Proportion

Two quantities are in **direct proportion** if they increase or decrease in the same ratio, or at the same rate.

If y is directly proportional to x, then $y \propto x$

When two variables are **directly proportional** they form a **straight line graph** that passes through the origin.

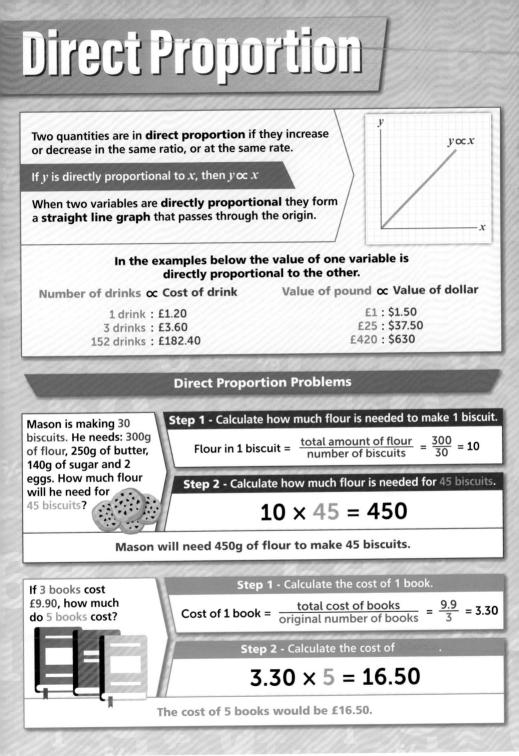

y

$y \propto x$

x

In the examples below the value of one variable is directly proportional to the other.

Number of drinks $\propto$ Cost of drink

1 drink : £1.20
3 drinks : £3.60
152 drinks : £182.40

Value of pound $\propto$ Value of dollar

£1 : $1.50
£25 : $37.50
£420 : $630

Direct Proportion Problems

Mason is making 30 biscuits. He needs: 300g of flour, 250g of butter, 140g of sugar and 2 eggs. How much flour will he need for 45 biscuits?

Step 1 - Calculate how much flour is needed to make 1 biscuit.

Flour in 1 biscuit = $\dfrac{\text{total amount of flour}}{\text{number of biscuits}} = \dfrac{300}{30} = 10$

Step 2 - Calculate how much flour is needed for 45 biscuits.

$$10 \times 45 = 450$$

Mason will need 450g of flour to make 45 biscuits.

If 3 books cost £9.90, how much do 5 books cost?

Step 1 - Calculate the cost of 1 book.

Cost of 1 book = $\dfrac{\text{total cost of books}}{\text{original number of books}} = \dfrac{9.9}{3} = 3.30$

Step 2 - Calculate the cost of 5 books.

$$3.30 \times 5 = 16.50$$

The cost of 5 books would be £16.50.

Inverse Proportion

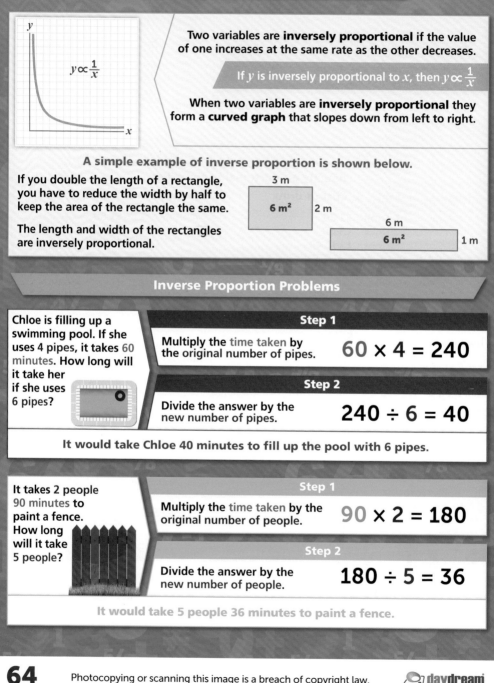

$y \propto \frac{1}{x}$

Two variables are **inversely proportional** if the value of one increases at the same rate as the other decreases.

If y is inversely proportional to x, then $y \propto \frac{1}{x}$

When two variables are **inversely proportional** they form a **curved graph** that slopes down from left to right.

A simple example of inverse proportion is shown below.

If you double the length of a rectangle, you have to reduce the width by half to keep the area of the rectangle the same.

The length and width of the rectangles are inversely proportional.

3 m

6 m²   2 m

6 m

6 m²   1 m

Inverse Proportion Problems

Chloe is filling up a swimming pool. If she uses 4 pipes, it takes 60 minutes. How long will it take her if she uses 6 pipes?

Step 1

Multiply the time taken by the original number of pipes.

$60 \times 4 = 240$

Step 2

Divide the answer by the new number of pipes.

$240 \div 6 = 40$

It would take Chloe 40 minutes to fill up the pool with 6 pipes.

It takes 2 people 90 minutes to paint a fence. How long will it take 5 people?

Step 1

Multiply the time taken by the original number of people.

$90 \times 2 = 180$

Step 2

Divide the answer by the new number of people.

$180 \div 5 = 36$

It would take 5 people 36 minutes to paint a fence.

daydream EDUCATION

Proportion Equations

Direct and inverse proportion problems are often represented as equations. Proportion equations include a constant, k, known as the proportionality constant.

Proportion		Equation
y is directly proportional to x.	$y \propto x$	$y = kx$
y is inversely proportional to x.	$y \propto \frac{1}{x}$	$y = \frac{k}{x}$
y is directly proportional to the cube of p.	$y \propto p^3$	$y = kp^3$
y is inversely proportional to the square of r.	$y \propto \frac{1}{r^2}$	$y = \frac{k}{r^2}$
y is directly proportional to the square root of d.	$y \propto \sqrt{d}$	$y = k\sqrt{d}$

Solving Proportion Problems Algebraically

Example 1

a is inversely proportional to the square of b when $a = 16$ and $b = 2$.

Calculate the value of a when $b = 3$.

1 Represent the statement as a proportion and then convert it to an equation.

$$a \propto \frac{1}{b^2} \qquad a = \frac{k}{b^2}$$

2 Substitute the original values of a and b into the equation, and solve to find the value of k.

$$16 = \frac{k}{2^2}$$
$$16 = \frac{k}{4}$$
$$64 = k$$

3 To find the value of a, when $b = 3$, substitute the values of b (3) and k (64) into the equation and solve.

$$a = \frac{k}{b^2}$$
$$a = \frac{64}{3^2}$$
$$a = \frac{64}{9}$$
$$a = 7.\dot{1}$$

Example 2

An elastic band (e) stretches proportionally to the force (f) applied to it. If 20 N produces an increase in length of 4 cm, what force will produce an increase in length of 7.5 cm?

1 Represent the statement as a proportion and then convert it to an equation.

$$e \propto f \qquad e = kf$$

2 Substitute the values of e and f into the equation, and solve to find the value of k.

$$4 = k20$$
$$\frac{4}{20} = k$$
$$0.2 = k$$

3 To find the value of f, when $e = 7.5$, substitute the values of e (7.5) and k (0.2) into the equation and solve.

$$e = kf$$
$$7.5 = 0.2 \times f$$
$$\frac{7.5}{0.2} = f$$
$$37.5 = f$$

Percentages

The word percent comes from the Latin words *per* and *cent* meaning 'out of every 100'. The symbol for percent is %.

Finding a Percentage

What is 20% of 40?

Method 1 - Convert to a Decimal

1. Convert the percentage into a decimal.

$$20 \div 100 = 0.2$$

2. Multiply the amount by the decimal.

$$40 \times 0.2 = 8$$

20% of 40 is 8

Method 2 - Finding 10%

1. Find 10% by dividing the amount by 10.

$$40 \div 10 = 4$$

2. Multiply the answer by 2 to get 20%.

$$4 \times 2 = 8$$

20% of 40 is 8

For more complex calculations you can use the finding 1% method.

What is 24% of 250?

1. Find 1% by dividing the amount by 100.

$$250 \div 100 = 2.5$$

2. Multiply the answer by 24 to get 24%.

$$2.5 \times 24 = 60$$

24% of 250 is 60

Expressing One Quantity as a Percentage of Another

Percentages are used to express how large or small one amount is relative to another amount. For example, percentages are often used to express exam results.

Harry scored 30 out of 50 in his maths exam.
What is his score as a percentage?

1. Divide Harry's score by the total number of questions.

$$\frac{30}{50} = 0.6$$

2. Multiply the answer by 100.

$$0.6 \times 100 = 60$$

Harry scored 60% in his maths exam.

Evie is practicing her penalties. She scores 24 out of 30.
What is her success rate as a percentage?

1. Divide Evie's score by the total number of penalties.

$$\frac{24}{30} = 0.8$$

2. Multiply the answer by 100.

$$0.8 \times 100 = 80$$

Evie scored 80% of her penalties.

daydream
EDUCATION

Percentage Change

Percentage Increase

Find the value of the percentage and **add** it to the original amount.

Repairs to Charlie's car cost £250 + VAT (20%). What is the cost including VAT?

1 Calculate 20%.
20% of 250 = 50

2 Add it to the original amount.
250 + 50 = 300

The total cost of the repairs is **£300**.

Percentage Decrease

Find the value of the percentage and **subtract** it from the original amount.

A £40 dress has 10% off in the sale. What is the sale price of the dress?

1 Calculate 10%.
10% of 40 = 4

2 Subtract it from the original amount.
40 − 4 = 36

The sale price of the dress is **£36**.

Reverse Percentages: Finding the Original Value

A house **increases** in value by 16% to £278,400. What was its original value?

Original value = 100% £278,400 = 116%	1. Write the amount as a percentage of the original value.	Original value = 100% £9,187.50 = 75%
278,400 ÷ 116 = 2,400	2. Divide the amount by the percentage to find 1% of the original value.	9,187.50 ÷ 75 = 122.50
2,400 × 100 = 240,000	3. Multiply by 100.	122.50 × 100 = 12,250

A car **decreases** in value by 25% to £9,187.50. What was its original value?

The original value of the house was **£240,000**.

The original value of the car was **£12,250**.

Percentage Change

$$\text{Percentage change} = \frac{\text{Change in value}}{\text{Original value}} \times 100$$

Last year Sienna had £3,200 in her bank account. She now has £3,360 despite not having paid in any money.

Calculate the rate of interest on her account.

1 Calculate the change in value (balance).
3,360 − 3,200 = 160

2 Divide the change in balance by the original balance.
160 ÷ 3,200 = 0.05

3 Multiply by 100.
0.05 × 100 = 5

The rate of interest on Sienna's account was **5%**.

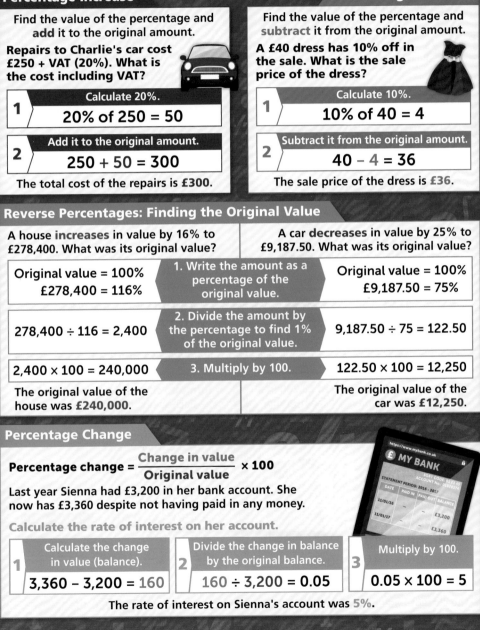

Compound Growth & Decay

Compound growth and decay can be calculated using the following formula:

$$A = P\left(1 \pm \frac{r}{100}\right)^n$$

+ for growth
– for decay

A   amount accrued

P   principal (original amount)

r   rate of interest

n   number of times that the interest is compounded

Compound Growth

Bacteria multiply at a rate of 100% per hour. If there is one bacterium to begin, how many bacteria will there be after ten hours?

$A = P\left(1 + \dfrac{r}{100}\right)^n$

$\quad = 1\left(1 + \dfrac{100}{100}\right)^{10}$

$\quad = 1(1 + 1)^{10}$

$\quad = 1(2)^{10}$

$\quad = 1 \times 1,024$

$A = 1,024$

The number of bacteria after 10 hours is 1,024.

Five years ago, Evie invested £3,200 in a bank account that pays 2% compound interest per annum. How much money is currently in the account if she has not withdrawn any money?

$A = P\left(1 + \dfrac{r}{100}\right)^n$

$\quad = 3,200\left(1 + \dfrac{2}{100}\right)^5$

$\quad = 3,200(1 + 0.02)^5$

$\quad = 3,200(1.02)^5$

$\quad = 3,200 \times 1.1040808032$

$A = 3,533.06$ (2 d.p.)

The current bank balance is £3,533.06.

Compound Decay

Jessica bought a car for £16,000. If the car depreciates by 14% each year, how much will it be worth in three years?

$A = P\left(1 - \dfrac{r}{100}\right)^n$

$\quad = 16,000\left(1 - \dfrac{14}{100}\right)^3$

$\quad = 16,000(1 - 0.14)^3$

$\quad = 16,000(0.86)^3$

$\quad = 16,000 \times 0.636056$

$A = 10,176.90$ (2 d.p.)

In three years, the car will be worth £10,176.90.

A furniture shop is holding a clearance sale. Each week, prices are reduced by 20%. Before the sale, a table was £450. How much will the table cost at the end of the third week?

$A = P\left(1 - \dfrac{r}{100}\right)^n$

$\quad = 450\left(1 - \dfrac{20}{100}\right)^3$

$\quad = 450(1 - 0.2)^3$

$\quad = 450(0.8)^3$

$\quad = 450 \times 0.512$

$A = 230.40$

FURNITURE STORE

The price of the table at the end of the third week is £230.40.

Compound Measures

A compound measure is made up of two or more other measures.

Speed

Speed is a measure of the distance travelled per unit time.

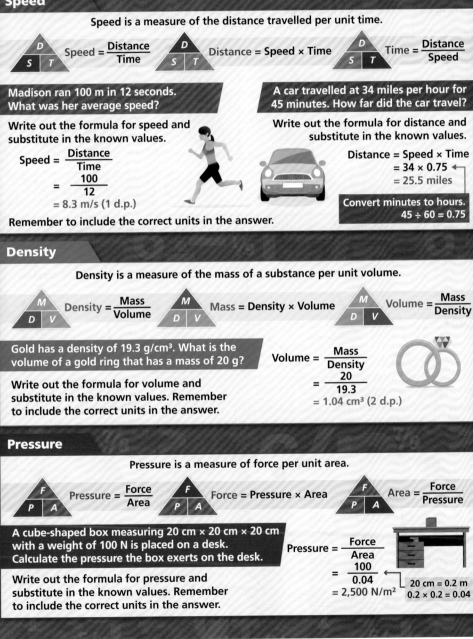

$$\text{Speed} = \frac{\text{Distance}}{\text{Time}}$$

$$\text{Distance} = \text{Speed} \times \text{Time}$$

$$\text{Time} = \frac{\text{Distance}}{\text{Speed}}$$

Madison ran 100 m in 12 seconds. What was her average speed?

Write out the formula for speed and substitute in the known values.

$$\text{Speed} = \frac{\text{Distance}}{\text{Time}}$$

$$= \frac{100}{12}$$

$$= 8.3 \text{ m/s (1 d.p.)}$$

Remember to include the correct units in the answer.

A car travelled at 34 miles per hour for 45 minutes. How far did the car travel?

Write out the formula for distance and substitute in the known values.

$$\text{Distance} = \text{Speed} \times \text{Time}$$

$$= 34 \times 0.75$$

$$= 25.5 \text{ miles}$$

Convert minutes to hours.
$45 \div 60 = 0.75$

Density

Density is a measure of the mass of a substance per unit volume.

$$\text{Density} = \frac{\text{Mass}}{\text{Volume}}$$

$$\text{Mass} = \text{Density} \times \text{Volume}$$

$$\text{Volume} = \frac{\text{Mass}}{\text{Density}}$$

Gold has a density of 19.3 g/cm³. What is the volume of a gold ring that has a mass of 20 g?

Write out the formula for volume and substitute in the known values. Remember to include the correct units in the answer.

$$\text{Volume} = \frac{\text{Mass}}{\text{Density}}$$

$$= \frac{20}{19.3}$$

$$= 1.04 \text{ cm}^3 \text{ (2 d.p.)}$$

Pressure

Pressure is a measure of force per unit area.

$$\text{Pressure} = \frac{\text{Force}}{\text{Area}}$$

$$\text{Force} = \text{Pressure} \times \text{Area}$$

$$\text{Area} = \frac{\text{Force}}{\text{Pressure}}$$

A cube-shaped box measuring 20 cm × 20 cm × 20 cm with a weight of 100 N is placed on a desk. Calculate the pressure the box exerts on the desk.

Write out the formula for pressure and substitute in the known values. Remember to include the correct units in the answer.

$$\text{Pressure} = \frac{\text{Force}}{\text{Area}}$$

$$= \frac{100}{0.04}$$

$$= 2,500 \text{ N/m}^2$$

20 cm = 0.2 m
0.2 × 0.2 = 0.04

Angles and Their Measurement

The turn, or rotation, between two meeting lines is called an angle. Angles are measured in degrees (°), often with a protractor or angle measurer.

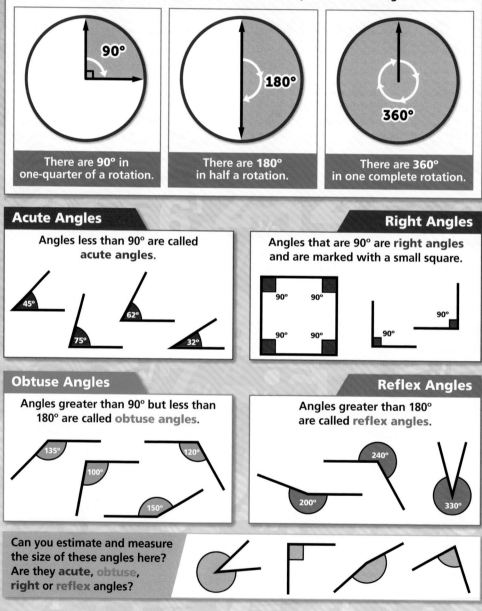

90°

There are **90°** in one-quarter of a rotation.

180°

There are **180°** in half a rotation.

360°

There are **360°** in one complete rotation.

Acute Angles

Angles less than 90° are called **acute angles**.

45°   62°   75°   32°

Right Angles

Angles that are 90° are **right angles** and are marked with a small square.

90°   90°   90°   90°   90°   90°

Obtuse Angles

Angles greater than 90° but less than 180° are called **obtuse angles**.

135°   120°   100°   150°

Reflex Angles

Angles greater than 180° are called **reflex angles**.

240°   200°   330°

Can you estimate and measure the size of these angles here? Are they **acute**, **obtuse**, **right** or **reflex** angles?

daydream EDUCATION

Angle Properties

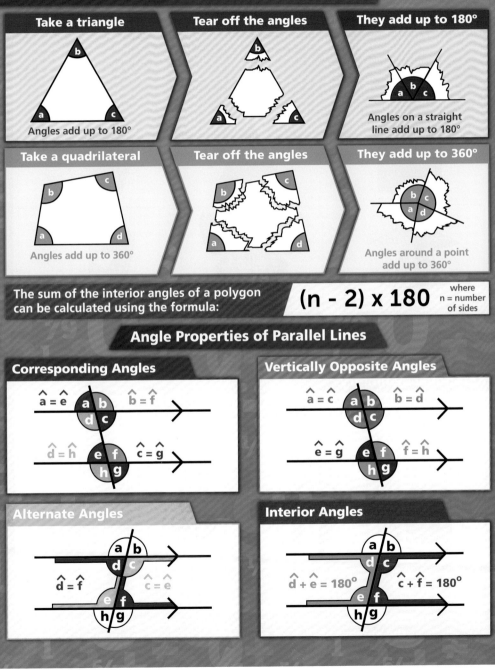

Take a triangle

b

a   c

Angles add up to 180°

Tear off the angles

b

a   c

They add up to 180°

a   b   c

Angles on a straight line add up to 180°

Take a quadrilateral

b   c

a   d

Angles add up to 360°

Tear off the angles

b   c

a   d

They add up to 360°

b   c
a   d

Angles around a point add up to 360°

The sum of the interior angles of a polygon can be calculated using the formula:

$$(n - 2) \times 180$$

where n = number of sides

Angle Properties of Parallel Lines

Corresponding Angles

$\hat{a} = \hat{e}$ a b / d c $\hat{b} = \hat{f}$

$\hat{d} = \hat{h}$ e f / h g $\hat{c} = \hat{g}$

Vertically Opposite Angles

$\hat{a} = \hat{c}$ a b / d c $\hat{b} = \hat{d}$

$\hat{e} = \hat{g}$ e f / h g $\hat{f} = \hat{h}$

Alternate Angles

a b / d c

$\hat{d} = \hat{f}$ $\hat{c} = \hat{e}$

e f / h g

Interior Angles

a b / d c

$\hat{d} + \hat{e} = 180°$ $\hat{c} + \hat{f} = 180°$

e f / h g

Symmetry

Line Symmetry

A line of symmetry, also known as a line of reflection, divides an object into two parts that are the same size and shape.

A **square** has **4** lines of symmetry.

An **equilateral triangle** has **3** lines of symmetry.

A **regular pentagon** has **5** lines of symmetry.

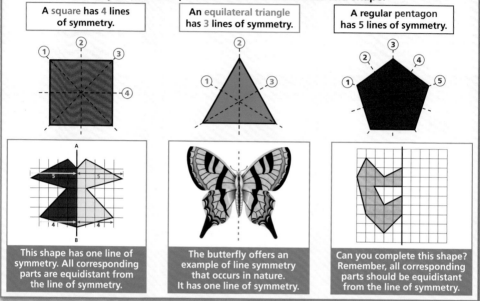

This shape has one line of symmetry. All corresponding parts are equidistant from the line of symmetry.

The butterfly offers an example of line symmetry that occurs in nature. It has one line of symmetry.

Can you complete this shape? Remember, all corresponding parts should be equidistant from the line of symmetry.

Rotational Symmetry

An object has rotational symmetry if it returns to its original form at any point when it is rotated around a central point. Shapes that have no rotational symmetry have rotational symmetry of order 1.

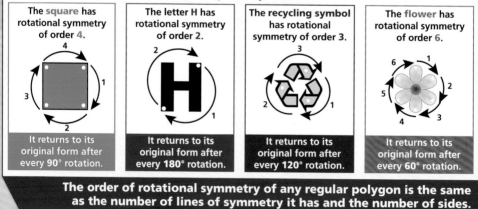

The **square** has rotational symmetry of order **4**.

It returns to its original form after every **90°** rotation.

The letter **H** has rotational symmetry of order **2**.

It returns to its original form after every **180°** rotation.

The **recycling symbol** has rotational symmetry of order **3**.

It returns to its original form after every **120°** rotation.

The **flower** has rotational symmetry of order **6**.

It returns to its original form after every **60°** rotation.

The order of rotational symmetry of any regular polygon is the same as the number of lines of symmetry it has and the number of sides.

daydream EDUCATION

Polygons

Polygons are 2D shapes that have three sides or more, are made of straight lines and are closed (no open sides).

Regular Polygons

A polygon is regular if all of its sides and interior angles are equal.

Triangle

3 sides, 3 equal angles

Quadrilateral

4 sides, 4 equal angles

Pentagon

5 sides, 5 equal angles

Octagon

8 sides, 8 equal angles

Irregular Polygons

An irregular polygon can have sides of any length and interior angles of any size.

Triangle

Hexagon

Quadrilateral

Heptagon

Pentagon

Octagon

Sum of Interior Angles

Any polygon can be broken down into a number of triangles. Dividing a polygon up in this way can help you calculate the sum of it's internal angles.

The internal angles of a triangle add up to **180°**. Therefore, the sum of the internal angles of a polygon can be calculated by splitting it up into triangles and multiplying the number of triangles by 180.

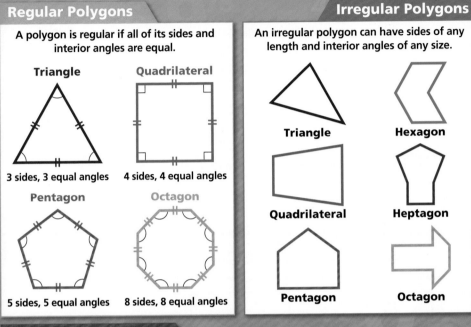

Triangle

180°

3 sides, 1 triangle
$1 \times 180° = 180°$

Quadrilateral

180°
180°

4 sides, 2 triangles
$2 \times 180° = 360°$

Pentagon

180°
180°
180°

5 sides, 3 triangles
$3 \times 180° = 540°$

Hexagon

180°
180°
180°
180°

6 sides, 4 triangles
$4 \times 180° = 720°$

The number of triangles in a polygon is always 2 less than its number of sides. Therefore, the following formula can be used to calculate the sum of interior angles of a polygon:

Sum of interior angles = 180(n-2) where **n** = number of sides

Triangles and Quadrilaterals

Triangles

Triangles have 3 sides and 3 angles. Their interior angles always add up to 180°.

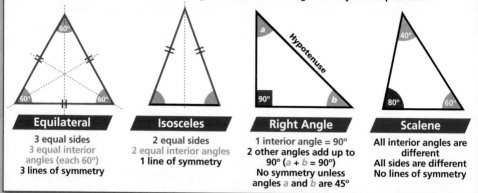

Equilateral
3 equal sides
3 equal interior angles (each 60°)
3 lines of symmetry

Isosceles
2 equal sides
2 equal interior angles
1 line of symmetry

Right Angle
1 interior angle = 90°
2 other angles add up to 90° ($a + b$ = 90°)
No symmetry unless angles a and b are 45°

Scalene
All interior angles are different
All sides are different
No lines of symmetry

Quadrilaterals

Quadrilaterals have 4 sides and 4 angles. Their interior angles always add up to 360°.

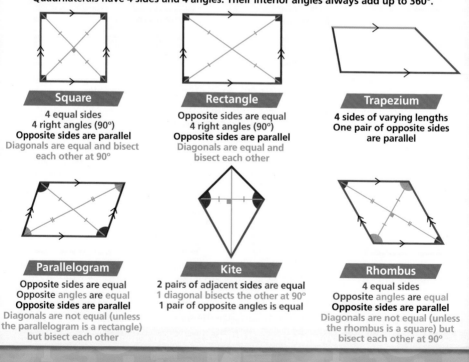

Square
4 equal sides
4 right angles (90°)
Opposite sides are parallel
Diagonals are equal and bisect each other at 90°

Rectangle
Opposite sides are equal
4 right angles (90°)
Opposite sides are parallel
Diagonals are equal and bisect each other

Trapezium
4 sides of varying lengths
One pair of opposite sides are parallel

Parallelogram
Opposite sides are equal
Opposite angles are equal
Opposite sides are parallel
Diagonals are not equal (unless the parallelogram is a rectangle) but bisect each other

Kite
2 pairs of adjacent sides are equal
1 diagonal bisects the other at 90°
1 pair of opposite angles is equal

Rhombus
4 equal sides
Opposite angles are equal
Opposite sides are parallel
Diagonals are not equal (unless the rhombus is a square) but bisect each other at 90°

Congruent Triangles

If two shapes are congruent, they are identical in both shape and size.

Two triangles are congruent if one of the following conditions applies:

SSS (Side-Side-Side)

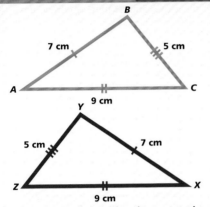

If three sides of one triangle are equal to three sides of another triangle, the triangles are congruent. This means that all angles are also the same.

SAS (Side-Angle-Side)

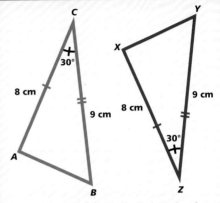

If two sides and the included angle of one triangle are equal to the corresponding sides and angle of another triangle, the triangles are congruent.

ASA (Angle-Side-Angle)

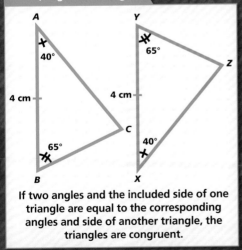

If two angles and the included side of one triangle are equal to the corresponding angles and side of another triangle, the triangles are congruent.

RHS (Right Angle-Hypotenuse-Side)

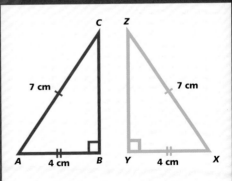

If the hypotenuse and one side of one triangle are equal to the corresponding hypotenuse and angle of another triangle, the triangles are congruent.

Transformations

Translation

A translation moves every point on a shape the same distance in the same direction.

Shape **A** has been translated +3 units along the x-axis **and** +2 units up the y-axis.

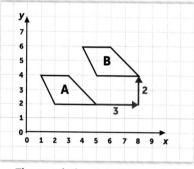

The translation **A** to **B** expressed as a vector is $\begin{bmatrix} 3 \\ 2 \end{bmatrix}$.

Shape **C** has been translated -6 units along the x-axis **and** +3 units up the y-axis.

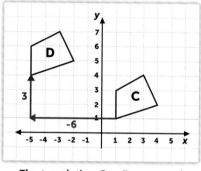

The translation **C** to **D** expressed as a vector is $\begin{bmatrix} -6 \\ 3 \end{bmatrix}$.

In a translation, the shapes are congruent. This means that one shape can be turned, flipped or moved so it fits exactly on the other.

Reflection

A reflection produces a mirror image of a shape along a line of reflection.

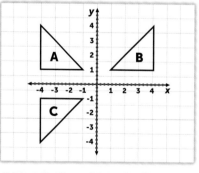

B is a reflection of **A** across the y-axis.
C is a reflection of **A** across the x-axis.

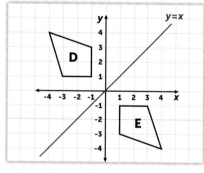

Shape **E** is a reflection of shape **D** in the line y=x.

In a reflection, the shapes are congruent. This means that one shape can be turned, flipped or moved so it fits exactly on the other.

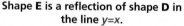

Rotation

A rotation turns a shape about a fixed point.
To perform a rotation, three details are needed:

1 The centre of rotation   **2** The angle of rotation   **3** The direction of rotation

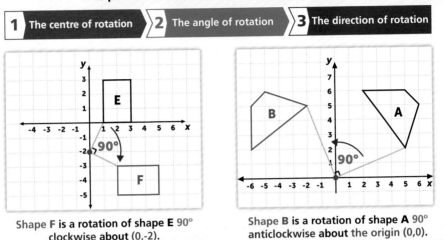

Shape **F** is a rotation of shape **E** 90°
clockwise about (0,-2).

Shape **B** is a rotation of shape **A** 90°
anticlockwise about the origin (0,0).

In a rotation, the shapes are congruent. This means that one shape can be turned, flipped or
moved so it fits exactly on the other.

Enlargement

To perform an enlargement, two pieces of information are needed:

1 The centre of enlargement – the point from which the object is enlarged   **2** The scale factor – the size of the enlargement

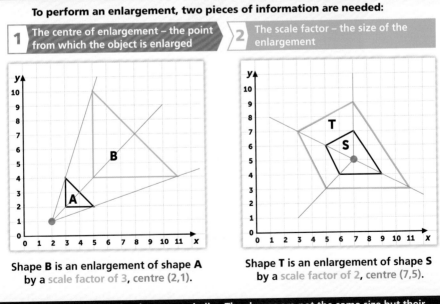

Shape **B** is an enlargement of shape **A**
by a scale factor of 3, centre (2,1).

Shape **T** is an enlargement of shape **S**
by a scale factor of 2, centre (7,5).

In an enlargement, the shapes are similar. The shapes are not the same size but their
angles are the same size and their lengths are proportionate to each other.

Circle Properties

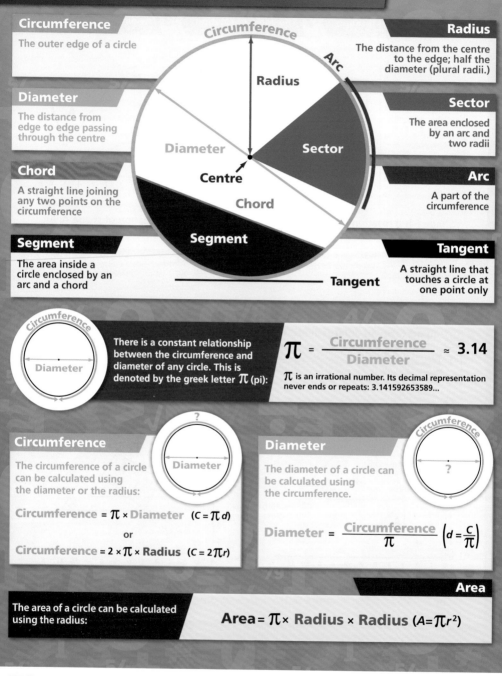

Circumference
The outer edge of a circle

Diameter
The distance from edge to edge passing through the centre

Chord
A straight line joining any two points on the circumference

Segment
The area inside a circle enclosed by an arc and a chord

Radius
The distance from the centre to the edge; half the diameter (plural radii.)

Sector
The area enclosed by an arc and two radii

Arc
A part of the circumference

Tangent
A straight line that touches a circle at one point only

There is a constant relationship between the circumference and diameter of any circle. This is denoted by the greek letter π (pi):

$$\pi = \frac{\text{Circumference}}{\text{Diameter}} \approx 3.14$$

π is an irrational number. Its decimal representation never ends or repeats: 3.141592653589...

Circumference
The circumference of a circle can be calculated using the diameter or the radius:

Circumference = π × Diameter $(C = \pi d)$

or

Circumference = 2 × π × Radius $(C = 2\pi r)$

Diameter
The diameter of a circle can be calculated using the circumference.

Diameter = $\dfrac{\text{Circumference}}{\pi}$ $\left(d = \dfrac{C}{\pi}\right)$

Area
The area of a circle can be calculated using the radius:

Area = π × Radius × Radius $(A = \pi r^2)$

daydream EDUCATION

The length of an arc can be calculated using the following formula:

$$\text{Length of Arc} = \frac{\text{Angle}}{360} \times \text{Circumference}$$

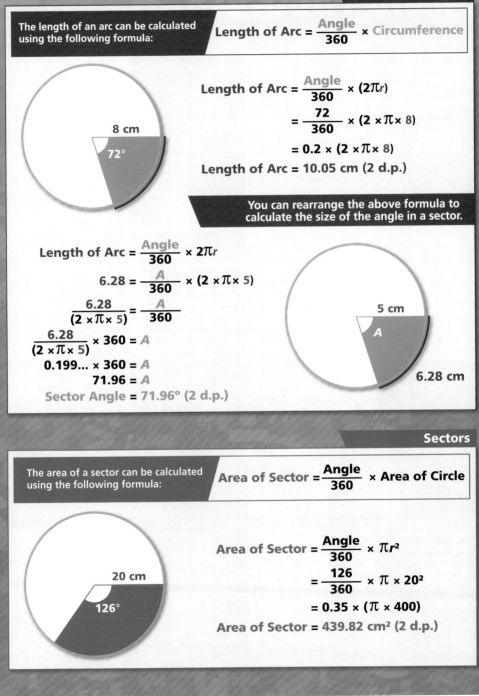

$$\text{Length of Arc} = \frac{\text{Angle}}{360} \times (2\pi r)$$

$$= \frac{72}{360} \times (2 \times \pi \times 8)$$

$$= 0.2 \times (2 \times \pi \times 8)$$

$$\text{Length of Arc} = 10.05 \text{ cm (2 d.p.)}$$

You can rearrange the above formula to calculate the size of the angle in a sector.

$$\text{Length of Arc} = \frac{\text{Angle}}{360} \times 2\pi r$$

$$6.28 = \frac{A}{360} \times (2 \times \pi \times 5)$$

$$\frac{6.28}{(2 \times \pi \times 5)} = \frac{A}{360}$$

$$\frac{6.28}{(2 \times \pi \times 5)} \times 360 = A$$

$$0.199... \times 360 = A$$

$$71.96 = A$$

Sector Angle = 71.96° (2 d.p.)

Sectors

The area of a sector can be calculated using the following formula:

$$\text{Area of Sector} = \frac{\text{Angle}}{360} \times \text{Area of Circle}$$

$$\text{Area of Sector} = \frac{\text{Angle}}{360} \times \pi r^2$$

$$= \frac{126}{360} \times \pi \times 20^2$$

$$= 0.35 \times (\pi \times 400)$$

$$\text{Area of Sector} = 439.82 \text{ cm}^2 \text{ (2 d.p.)}$$

Circle Theorems

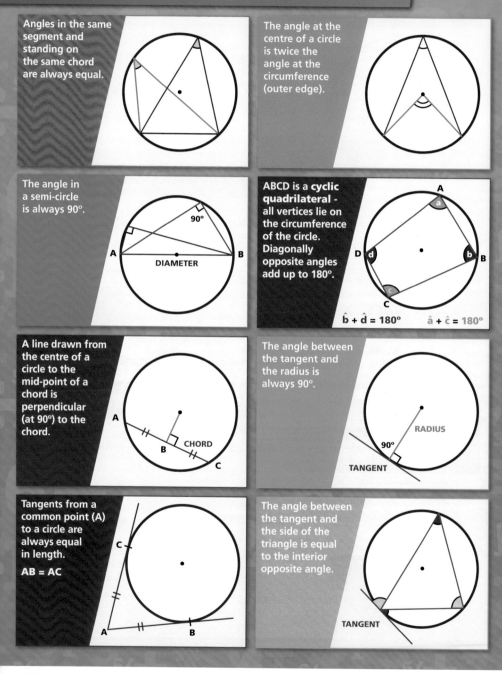

Angles in the same segment and standing on the same chord are always equal.

The angle at the centre of a circle is twice the angle at the circumference (outer edge).

The angle in a semi-circle is always 90°.

90°

A   B

DIAMETER

ABCD is a cyclic quadrilateral - all vertices lie on the circumference of the circle. Diagonally opposite angles add up to 180°.

A
a
D d
B b
C c

$\hat{b} + \hat{d} = 180°$ $\hat{a} + \hat{c} = 180°$

A line drawn from the centre of a circle to the mid-point of a chord is perpendicular (at 90°) to the chord.

A
B
CHORD
C

The angle between the tangent and the radius is always 90°.

RADIUS
90°
TANGENT

Tangents from a common point (A) to a circle are always equal in length.

AB = AC

C
A   B

The angle between the tangent and the side of the triangle is equal to the interior opposite angle.

TANGENT

Area

Area is the total size of a flat surface. It is the amount of space inside the perimeter.

Rectangle/Square

What is the area of the football field?

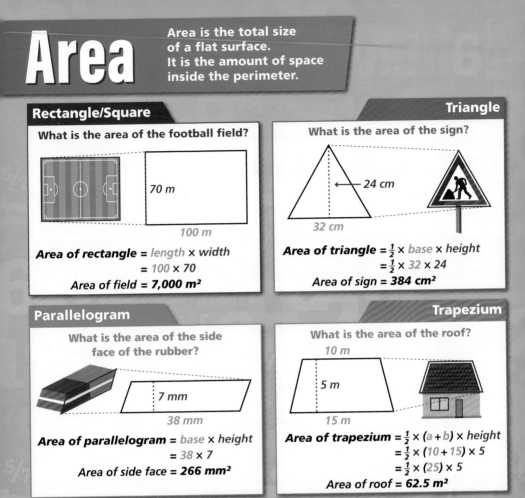

70 m

100 m

Area of rectangle = *length × width*
= *100 × 70*
Area of field = 7,000 m²

Triangle

What is the area of the sign?

← 24 cm

32 cm

Area of triangle = $\frac{1}{2}$ × *base × height*
= $\frac{1}{2}$ × *32 × 24*
Area of sign = 384 cm²

Parallelogram

What is the area of the side face of the rubber?

7 mm

38 mm

Area of parallelogram = *base × height*
= *38 × 7*
Area of side face = 266 mm²

Trapezium

What is the area of the roof?

10 m

5 m

15 m

Area of trapezium = $\frac{1}{2}$ × *(a + b) × height*
= $\frac{1}{2}$ × *(10 + 15) × 5*
= $\frac{1}{2}$ × *(25) × 5*
Area of roof = 62.5 m²

Compound Shapes

When measuring the area of a compound shape, break it down into simpler shapes and then add the areas together. Look at the plan of the room below.

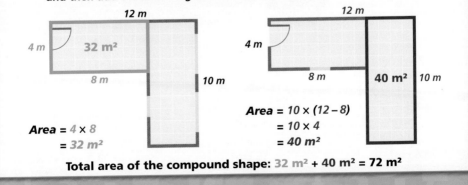

12 m

4 m

32 m²

8 m

10 m

Area = *4 × 8*
= *32 m²*

12 m

4 m

8 m

40 m²   10 m

Area = *10 × (12 − 8)*
= *10 × 4*
= *40 m²*

Total area of the compound shape: 32 m² + 40 m² = 72 m²

Volume

Volume is the amount of space inside a 3D shape or object.

3D Shapes

A solid 3D figure has faces, edges and vertices (corners).

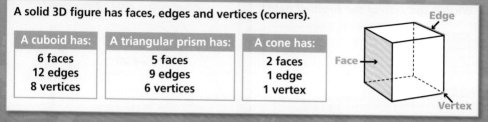

A cuboid has:	A triangular prism has:	A cone has:
6 faces	5 faces	2 faces
12 edges	9 edges	1 edge
8 vertices	6 vertices	1 vertex

Edge

Face →

Vertex

Prisms and Cylinders

Solid objects that maintain a constant cross-sectional area along their length.

Volume of prism or cylinder = cross-sectional area × length

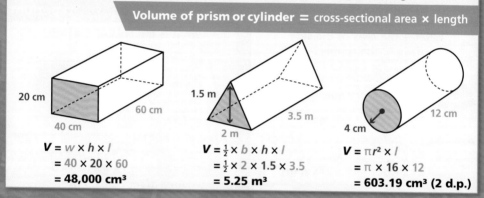

20 cm
60 cm
40 cm

$V = w \times h \times l$
$= 40 \times 20 \times 60$
$= 48{,}000 \text{ cm}^3$

1.5 m
3.5 m
2 m

$V = \frac{1}{2} \times b \times h \times l$
$= \frac{1}{2} \times 2 \times 1.5 \times 3.5$
$= 5.25 \text{ m}^3$

4 cm
12 cm

$V = \pi r^2 \times l$
$= \pi \times 16 \times 12$
$= 603.19 \text{ cm}^3 \text{ (2 d.p.)}$

Pyramids and Cones

3D shapes that narrow to a common vertex, creating a point.

Volume of pyramid or cone = $\frac{1}{3}$ area of base × height

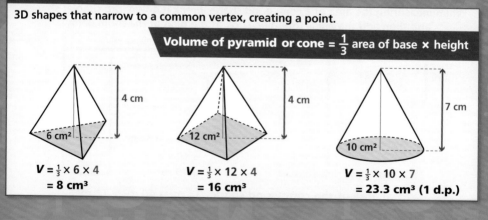

4 cm
6 cm²

$V = \frac{1}{3} \times 6 \times 4$
$= 8 \text{ cm}^3$

4 cm
12 cm²

$V = \frac{1}{3} \times 12 \times 4$
$= 16 \text{ cm}^3$

7 cm
10 cm²

$V = \frac{1}{3} \times 10 \times 7$
$= 23.3 \text{ cm}^3 \text{ (1 d.p.)}$

daydream EDUCATION

Spheres

A sphere is a perfectly round 3D shape. Every point on its surface is equidistant from its centre.

Volume of sphere $= \frac{4}{3}\pi r^3$

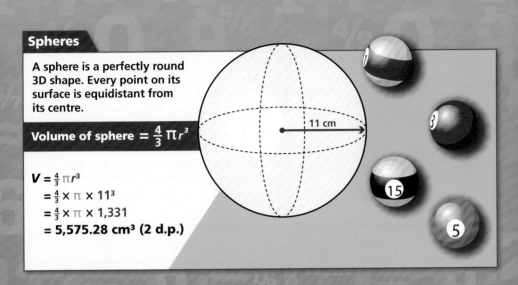

11 cm

$V = \frac{4}{3}\pi r^3$

$\quad = \frac{4}{3} \times \pi \times 11^3$

$\quad = \frac{4}{3} \times \pi \times 1,331$

$\quad = 5{,}575.28$ **cm³ (2 d.p.)**

Frustums

If the top section of a cone is cut off parallel to its circular base, it is possible to calculate the volume of the remaining shape, a frustum.

Volume of frustum = volume of original cone – volume of removed cone

$V = \frac{1}{3}\pi r^2 h - \frac{1}{3}\pi r^2 h$

$\quad = \frac{1}{3} \times \pi \times 2^2 \times 6 - \frac{1}{3} \times \pi \times 1^2 \times 3$

$\quad = \frac{1}{3} \times \pi \times 24 - \frac{1}{3} \times \pi \times 3$

$\quad = 25.13... - 3.14...$

$\quad = 21.99$ **cm³ (2 d.p.)**

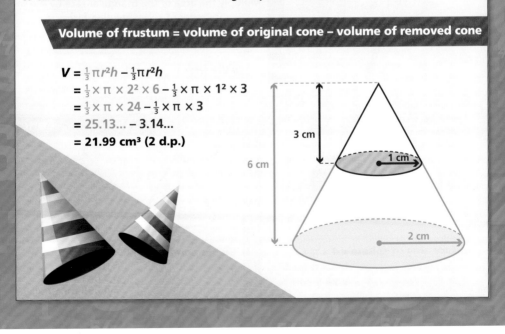

3 cm

1 cm

6 cm

2 cm

daydream
EDUCATION

Surface Area

Surface area is the total area of the outer surface of a 3D object. The surface area of a solid figure is equal to the total area of its net. To calculate the surface area of a shape, work out the area of each face and add them together.

Triangular Prism

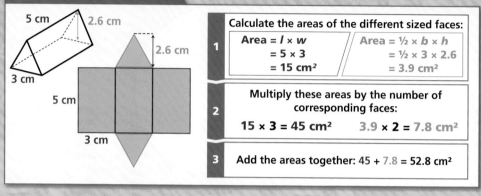

1 Calculate the areas of the different sized faces:

Area = $l \times w$	Area = $\frac{1}{2} \times b \times h$
$= 5 \times 3$	$= \frac{1}{2} \times 3 \times 2.6$
$= 15$ cm²	$= 3.9$ cm²

2 Multiply these areas by the number of corresponding faces:

$15 \times 3 = 45$ cm² $3.9 \times 2 = 7.8$ cm²

3 Add the areas together: $45 + 7.8 = 52.8$ cm²

Square-based Pyramid

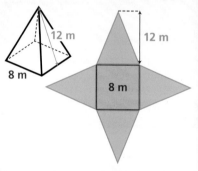

1 Calculate the areas of the different sized faces:

Area = $l \times w$	Area = $\frac{1}{2} \times b \times h$
$= 8 \times 8$	$= \frac{1}{2} \times 8 \times 12$
$= 64$ m²	$= 48$ m²

2 Multiply the area of the triangular face by the number of corresponding faces:

$48 \times 4 = 192$ m²

3 Add the areas together: $192 + 64 = 256$ m².

Sphere

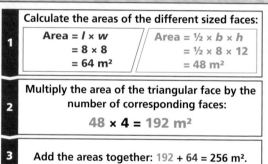

Surface area of sphere = $4 \times \pi \times r^2$
$= 4 \times \pi \times 2.5^2$
$= 78.5$ cm²

Cone

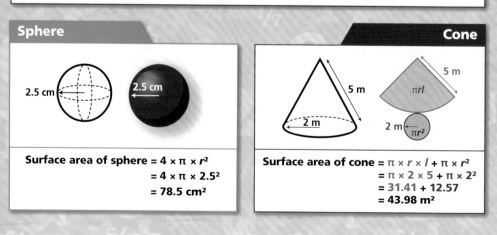

Surface area of cone = $\pi \times r \times l + \pi \times r^2$
$= \pi \times 2 \times 5 + \pi \times 2^2$
$= 31.41 + 12.57$
$= 43.98$ m²

Area & Volume Enlargements

Scale Factor

The size of an enlargement (or reduction) is described by its scale factor.

Scale factor = $\dfrac{\text{New length}}{\text{Old length}}$

Scale factor = $\dfrac{\text{New length}}{\text{Old length}}$

= $\dfrac{6}{2}$

= 3

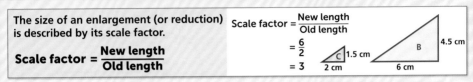

The scale factor of the enlargement **C** to **B** is 3. This can be displayed as a ratio: 1:3.

Area Scale Factor

Area scale factor = $\dfrac{\text{New area}}{\text{Old area}}$

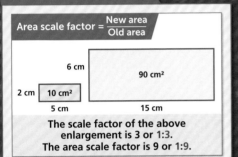

The scale factor of the above enlargement is 3 or 1:3.
The area scale factor is 9 or 1:9.

The **area scale factor** is the value of the linear scale factor squared.

Area scale factor = (Scale factor)²

Therefore, if the scale factor of an enlargement is 3, the area scale factor is 9. The sides are three times as long, and the area is nine times as big.

Volume Scale Factor

Volume scale factor = $\dfrac{\text{New volume}}{\text{Old volume}}$

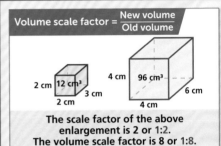

The scale factor of the above enlargement is 2 or 1:2.
The volume scale factor is 8 or 1:8.

The **volume scale factor** is the value of the linear scale factor cubed.

Volume scale factor = (Scale factor)³

Therefore, if the scale factor of an enlargement is 2, the volume scale factor is 8. The sides are twice as long, and the volume is eight times as big.

Example Question: What is the volume of the blue pyramid?

1 Find the scale factor:
Scale factor = $\dfrac{\text{New length}}{\text{Old length}} = \dfrac{6}{2} = 3$

2 Calculate the volume scale factor:
Volume scale factor = (Scale factor)³
= (3)³
= 27

3 Multiply this by the original volume:
4 m³ × 27 = 108 m³

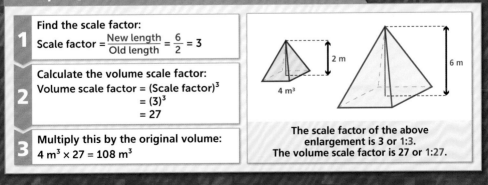

The scale factor of the above enlargement is 3 or 1:3.
The volume scale factor is 27 or 1:27.

Loci & Construction

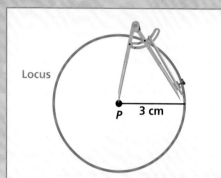

Locus

P   3 cm

The locus of points that are a fixed distance from a given point form a circle.

This is drawn using a compass. Set the compass to the required length (in this case 3 cm), place the compass point at *P* and draw a circle.

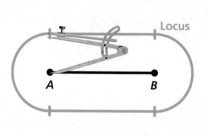

Locus

A   **B**

The locus of points that are a fixed distance from a given line form two parallel lines that are joined by semicircles at their ends.

The straight lines are drawn using a ruler, and the semicircle ends are drawn using a compass.

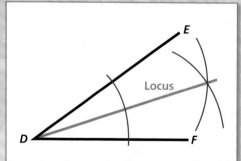

E

Locus

D   **F**

The locus of a point that is equidistant from two given lines that meet is an angle bisector.

This is drawn using a compass and a ruler. The compass needs to be kept the same length when marking the points.

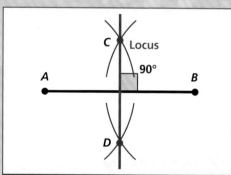

C Locus

90°

A   **B**

D

The locus of points that are equidistant from two given points is the perpendicular bisector of the line that joins the two points.

The locus (*CD*) is perpendicular (at a right angle) to the line that connects the two points (*AB*).

daydream
EDUCATION

Constructing Accurate 60° Angles

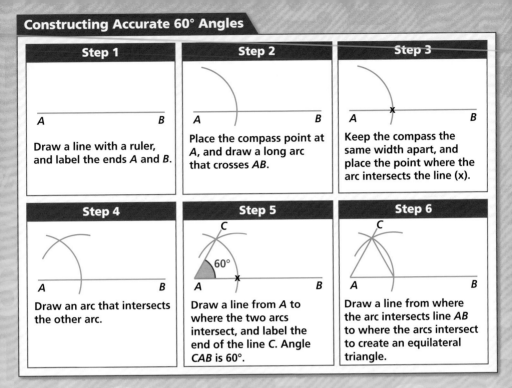

Step 1	Step 2	Step 3
Draw a line with a ruler, and label the ends *A* and *B*.	Place the compass point at *A*, and draw a long arc that crosses *AB*.	Keep the compass the same width apart, and place the point where the arc intersects the line (x).

Step 4	Step 5	Step 6
Draw an arc that intersects the other arc.	Draw a line from *A* to where the two arcs intersect, and label the end of the line *C*. Angle *CAB* is 60°.	Draw a line from where the arc intersects line *AB* to where the arcs intersect to create an equilateral triangle.

Constructing Accurate 90° Angles

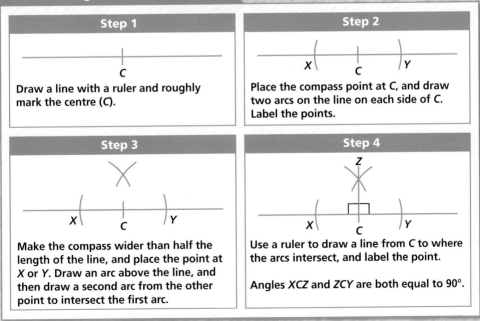

Step 1
Draw a line with a ruler and roughly mark the centre (*C*).

Step 2
Place the compass point at *C*, and draw two arcs on the line on each side of *C*. Label the points.

Step 3
Make the compass wider than half the length of the line, and place the point at *X* or *Y*. Draw an arc above the line, and then draw a second arc from the other point to intersect the first arc.

Step 4
Use a ruler to draw a line from *C* to where the arcs intersect, and label the point.

Angles *XCZ* and *ZCY* are both equal to 90°.

Elevations of 3D Shapes

Elevations are 2D representations of 3D objects.

Plans and Elevations of 3D Shapes

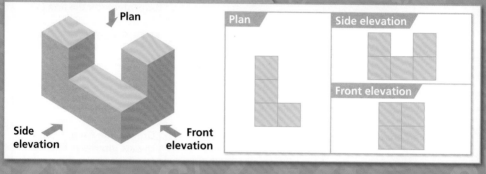

House

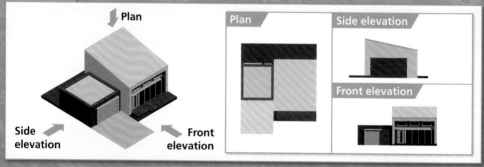

Van

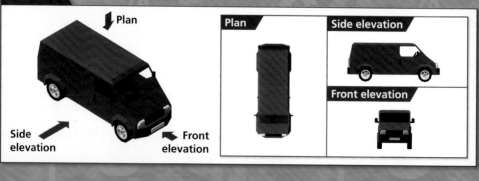

 daydream
EDUCATION

Three-Figure Bearings

A bearing is the direction of travel measured clockwise from the north line. All bearings are written using three figures (e.g. 050° rather than 50°).

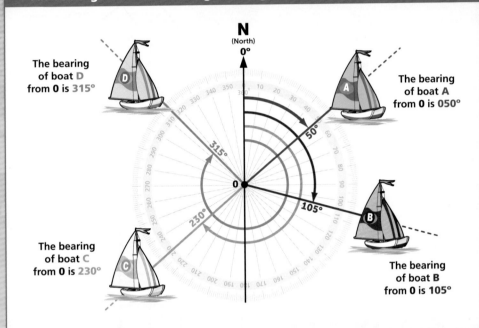

The bearing of boat D from 0 is 315°

The bearing of boat A from 0 is 050°

The bearing of boat C from 0 is 230°

The bearing of boat B from 0 is 105°

To find the bearing of the boat from the lifeguard station, follow the steps outlined below.

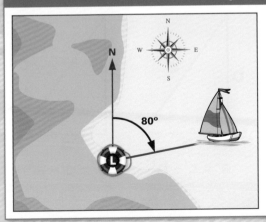

Step 1: Draw the north line at the lifeguard station (L).

Step 2: Draw a line from the lifeguard station to the boat.

Step 3: Measure the angle clockwise from the north line.

The size of the angle is **80°**. Therefore, the three-figure bearing of the boat from the lifeguard station is **080°**.

Pythagoras' Theorem

The square of the hypotenuse (the longest side, opposite the right angle), is equal to the sum of the squares of the other two sides.

Pythagoras discovered that when you draw a square onto each side of a right-angled triangle, the area of the two smaller squares added together, equals the area of the largest square.

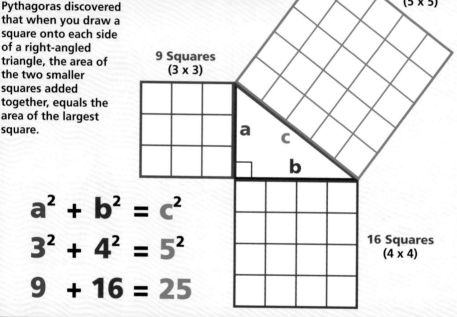

9 Squares (3 x 3)

25 Squares (5 x 5)

16 Squares (4 x 4)

$$a^2 + b^2 = c^2$$

$$3^2 + 4^2 = 5^2$$

$$9 + 16 = 25$$

When you know the lengths of any two sides, you can find the length of the third side.

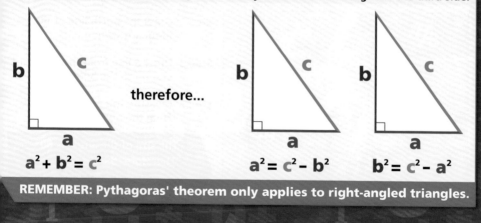

$$a^2 + b^2 = c^2$$

therefore...

$$a^2 = c^2 - b^2$$

$$b^2 = c^2 - a^2$$

REMEMBER: Pythagoras' theorem only applies to right-angled triangles.

3D Pythagoras

Pythagoras' theorem can be used to calculate unknown lengths in 3D shapes.

Scale Factor

Pythagoras' theorem is used to calculate the length of the longest diagonal in a cuboid.

To find the length of diagonal BH, follow the steps outlined below:

1 Use Pythagoras' theorem to calculate the length of **FH**. Do not find the square root of FH^2 as FH needs to be squared in the next step.

$FH^2 = FG^2 + GH^2$
$FH^2 = 4^2 + 12^2$
$FH^2 = 16 + 144$
$FH^2 = 160$

2 Use Pythagoras' theorem again to find the length of **BH**.

$BH^2 = BF^2 + FH^2$
$BH^2 = 6^2 + 160$
$BH^2 = 36 + 160$
$BH^2 = 196$
$BH = \sqrt{196}$
$BH = 14$ cm

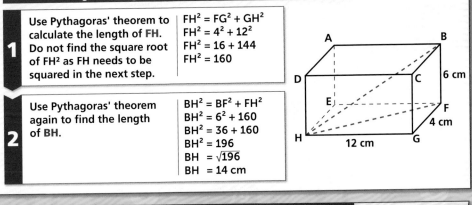

6 cm
4 cm
12 cm

Alternatively, the following formula can be used to calculate the length of the longest diagonal:

$a^2 + b^2 + c^2 = d^2$,
because $a^2 + b^2 = e^2$ and $e^2 + c^2 = d^2$

Try it for the example above:

$GH^2 + FG^2 + BF^2 = BH^2$
$12^2 + 4^2 + 6^2 = BH^2$
$\sqrt{196} = BH$
$14 = BH$

Other 3D Shapes

Pythagoras' theorem is also used to calculate unknown lengths in other 3D shapes.

To find the length of AD, follow the steps outlined below:

1 AD cannot be calculated unless the length of DF is known. Use Pythagoras' theorem to calculate the length of BD, and then halve it to find DF.

$BD^2 = BE^2 + DE^2$
$BD^2 = 4^2 + 8^2$
$BD^2 = 80$
$BD = \sqrt{80}$
$DF = \frac{1}{2}(4\sqrt{5})$
$DF = 2\sqrt{5}$

$\sqrt{80} = \sqrt{16} \times \sqrt{5} = 4\sqrt{5}$

2 Use Pythagoras' theorem again to find the length of **AD**.

$AD^2 = DF^2 + AF^2$
$AD^2 = (2\sqrt{5})^2 + 6^2$
$AD^2 = 20 + 36$
$AD^2 = 56$
$AD = \sqrt{56}$
$AD = 7.48$ m (2 d.p.)

$(2\sqrt{5})^2 = 4\sqrt{25} = 4 \times 5 = 20$

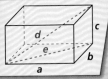
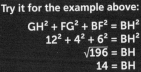

6 m
4 m
8 m

Trigonometry

Trigonometry deals with the relationship between the sides and angles of a triangle. In right-angled triangles, the following rules apply.

For the angle θ, the sides of the triangle are labelled as shown:

Opposite
The side opposite the angle θ.

Hypotenuse
The longest side. It is always opposite the right angle.

Adjacent
The side next to the angle θ.

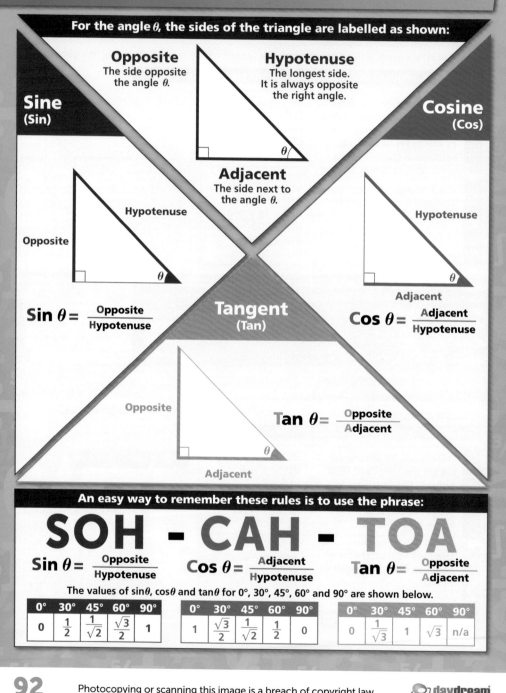

Sine (Sin)

$$Sin\ \theta = \frac{Opposite}{Hypotenuse}$$

Cosine (Cos)

$$Cos\ \theta = \frac{Adjacent}{Hypotenuse}$$

Tangent (Tan)

$$Tan\ \theta = \frac{Opposite}{Adjacent}$$

An easy way to remember these rules is to use the phrase:

SOH - CAH - TOA

$$Sin\ \theta = \frac{Opposite}{Hypotenuse}$$

$$Cos\ \theta = \frac{Adjacent}{Hypotenuse}$$

$$Tan\ \theta = \frac{Opposite}{Adjacent}$$

The values of sinθ, cosθ and tanθ for 0°, 30°, 45°, 60° and 90° are shown below.

0°	30°	45°	60°	90°
0	$\frac{1}{2}$	$\frac{1}{\sqrt{2}}$	$\frac{\sqrt{3}}{2}$	1

0°	30°	45°	60°	90°
1	$\frac{\sqrt{3}}{2}$	$\frac{1}{\sqrt{2}}$	$\frac{1}{2}$	0

0°	30°	45°	60°	90°
0	$\frac{1}{\sqrt{3}}$	1	$\sqrt{3}$	n/a

daydream EDUCATION

Trigonometry for All Triangles

Labelling the Triangle Is Vital

Side '*a*' is opposite angle '*A*'

Side '*b*' is opposite angle '*B*'

Side '*c*' is opposite angle '*C*'

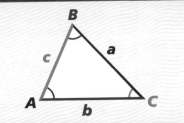

The Sine Rule

Used when you know **two angles** and a **side**. The sine rule for any triangle *ABC* is:

$$\frac{a}{\sin A} = \frac{b}{\sin B} = \frac{c}{\sin C}$$

To find the length of *YZ*, follow the steps outlined below.

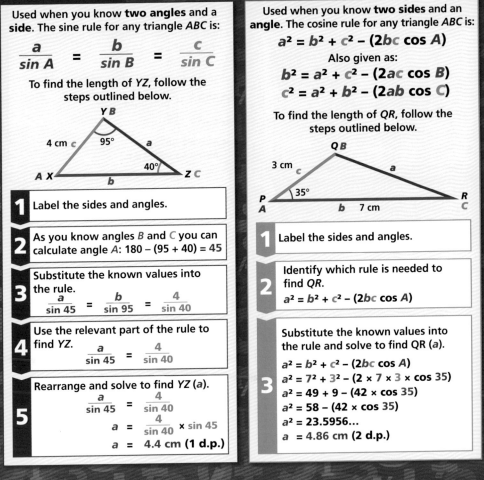

1 Label the sides and angles.

2 As you know angles *B* and *C* you can calculate angle *A*: 180 − (95 + 40) = 45

3 Substitute the known values into the rule.
$$\frac{a}{\sin 45} = \frac{b}{\sin 95} = \frac{4}{\sin 40}$$

4 Use the relevant part of the rule to find *YZ*.
$$\frac{a}{\sin 45} = \frac{4}{\sin 40}$$

5 Rearrange and solve to find *YZ* (*a*).
$$\frac{a}{\sin 45} = \frac{4}{\sin 40}$$
$$a = \frac{4}{\sin 40} \times \sin 45$$
$$a = 4.4 \text{ cm (1 d.p.)}$$

The Cosine Rule

Used when you know **two sides** and an **angle**. The cosine rule for any triangle *ABC* is:

$$a^2 = b^2 + c^2 - (2bc \cos A)$$

Also given as:

$$b^2 = a^2 + c^2 - (2ac \cos B)$$
$$c^2 = a^2 + b^2 - (2ab \cos C)$$

To find the length of *QR*, follow the steps outlined below.

1 Label the sides and angles.

2 Identify which rule is needed to find *QR*.
$$a^2 = b^2 + c^2 - (2bc \cos A)$$

3 Substitute the known values into the rule and solve to find QR (*a*).
$$a^2 = b^2 + c^2 - (2bc \cos A)$$
$$a^2 = 7^2 + 3^2 - (2 \times 7 \times 3 \times \cos 35)$$
$$a^2 = 49 + 9 - (42 \times \cos 35)$$
$$a^2 = 58 - (42 \times \cos 35)$$
$$a^2 = 23.5956...$$
$$a = 4.86 \text{ cm (2 d.p.)}$$

daydream
EDUCATION

3D Trigonometry

Trigonometry can be used to calculate unknown angles in 3D shapes, such as the angle between a line and a plane.

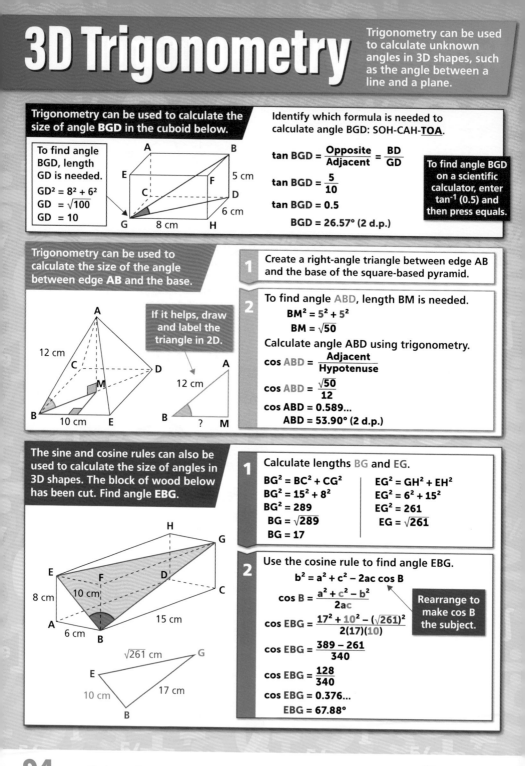

Trigonometry can be used to calculate the size of angle BGD in the cuboid below.

To find angle BGD, length GD is needed.

$GD^2 = 8^2 + 6^2$

$GD = \sqrt{100}$

$GD = 10$

Identify which formula is needed to calculate angle BGD: SOH-CAH-**TOA**.

$\tan BGD = \dfrac{\text{Opposite}}{\text{Adjacent}} = \dfrac{BD}{GD}$

$\tan BGD = \dfrac{5}{10}$

$\tan BGD = 0.5$

BGD = 26.57° (2 d.p.)

To find angle BGD on a scientific calculator, enter tan⁻¹ (0.5) and then press equals.

Trigonometry can be used to calculate the size of the angle between edge AB and the base.

1 Create a right-angle triangle between edge AB and the base of the square-based pyramid.

If it helps, draw and label the triangle in 2D.

2 To find angle ABD, length BM is needed.

$BM^2 = 5^2 + 5^2$

$BM = \sqrt{50}$

Calculate angle ABD using trigonometry.

$\cos ABD = \dfrac{\text{Adjacent}}{\text{Hypotenuse}}$

$\cos ABD = \dfrac{\sqrt{50}}{12}$

$\cos ABD = 0.589...$

ABD = 53.90° (2 d.p.)

The sine and cosine rules can also be used to calculate the size of angles in 3D shapes. The block of wood below has been cut. Find angle EBG.

1 Calculate lengths BG and EG.

$BG^2 = BC^2 + CG^2$

$BG^2 = 15^2 + 8^2$

$BG^2 = 289$

$BG = \sqrt{289}$

$BG = 17$

$EG^2 = GH^2 + EH^2$

$EG^2 = 6^2 + 15^2$

$EG^2 = 261$

$EG = \sqrt{261}$

2 Use the cosine rule to find angle EBG.

$b^2 = a^2 + c^2 - 2ac \cos B$

$\cos B = \dfrac{a^2 + c^2 - b^2}{2ac}$

Rearrange to make cos B the subject.

$\cos EBG = \dfrac{17^2 + 10^2 - (\sqrt{261})^2}{2(17)(10)}$

$\cos EBG = \dfrac{389 - 261}{340}$

$\cos EBG = \dfrac{128}{340}$

$\cos EBG = 0.376...$

EBG = 67.88°

---

daydream EDUCATION

Vectors

A vector is used to describe movement from one point to another. A vector has magnitude (how long it is) and direction. A scalar has magnitude only.

Vector Notation

A vector can be represented by a line segment (labelled with an arrow).

A vector between two points, A and B, is described as:

$$\overrightarrow{AB}, \quad a \quad \text{or} \quad \underline{a}$$

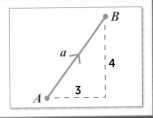

The vector can also be represented as a column vector: $\begin{pmatrix} 3 \\ 4 \end{pmatrix}$.

Multiplying Vectors by a Scalar

A vector can be multiplied by a scalar to change its magnitude but not its direction. In the example to the right, the vector $\underline{x}$ is multiplied by 2 to become $2\underline{x}$.

If the vector is negative, the direction of the arrow changes.

$\underline{a}$

$2\underline{a}$

$-2\underline{a}$

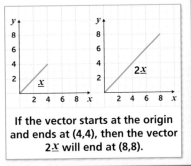

If the vector starts at the origin and ends at (4,4), then the vector $2\underline{x}$ will end at (8,8).

Addition and Subtraction of Vectors

Movements between points can be described by adding and subtracting vectors.

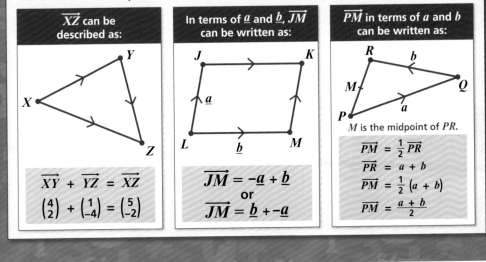

$\overrightarrow{XZ}$ can be described as:

$$\overrightarrow{XY} + \overrightarrow{YZ} = \overrightarrow{XZ}$$
$$\begin{pmatrix} 4 \\ 2 \end{pmatrix} + \begin{pmatrix} 1 \\ -4 \end{pmatrix} = \begin{pmatrix} 5 \\ -2 \end{pmatrix}$$

In terms of $\underline{a}$ and $\underline{b}$, $\overrightarrow{JM}$ can be written as:

$$\overrightarrow{JM} = -\underline{a} + \underline{b}$$
or
$$\overrightarrow{JM} = \underline{b} + -\underline{a}$$

$\overrightarrow{PM}$ in terms of a and b can be written as:

M is the midpoint of PR.

$$\overrightarrow{PM} = \tfrac{1}{2}\,\overrightarrow{PR}$$
$$\overrightarrow{PR} = a + b$$
$$\overrightarrow{PM} = \tfrac{1}{2}\,(a + b)$$
$$\overrightarrow{PM} = \frac{a + b}{2}$$

95

Probability

Probability is used in everyday life to predict the chances of things happening.

Probability Is Measured on a Scale of 0–1

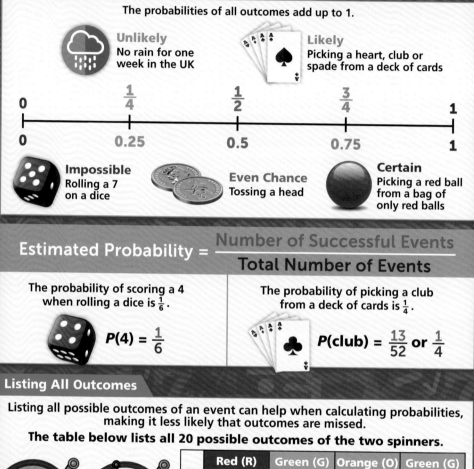

The probabilities of all outcomes add up to 1.

Unlikely
No rain for one week in the UK

Likely
Picking a heart, club or spade from a deck of cards

0	$\frac{1}{4}$	$\frac{1}{2}$	$\frac{3}{4}$	1
0	0.25	0.5	0.75	1

Impossible
Rolling a 7 on a dice

Even Chance
Tossing a head

Certain
Picking a red ball from a bag of only red balls

Estimated Probability = $\dfrac{\text{Number of Successful Events}}{\text{Total Number of Events}}$

The probability of scoring a 4 when rolling a dice is $\frac{1}{6}$.

$$P(4) = \frac{1}{6}$$

The probability of picking a club from a deck of cards is $\frac{1}{4}$.

$$P(\text{club}) = \frac{13}{52} \text{ or } \frac{1}{4}$$

Listing All Outcomes

Listing all possible outcomes of an event can help when calculating probabilities, making it less likely that outcomes are missed.

The table below lists all 20 possible outcomes of the two spinners.

	Red (R)	Green (G)	Orange (O)	Green (G)
1	1R	1G	1O	1G
2	2R	2G	2O	2G
3	3R	3G	3O	3G
5	5R	5G	5O	5G
1	1R	1G	1O	1G

The probability of spinning a 2 and a red (2R) is: $\frac{1}{20}$

The probability of spinning a 1 and a green (1G) is: $\frac{4}{20}$ or $\frac{1}{5}$

Independent and Dependent Events

The probability of picking a heart from a deck of cards is:

25% $\frac{13}{52}$ or $\frac{1}{4}$ **0.25**

Independent Events

Events are **independent** if the outcome of one event **does not** affect the outcome of another.

If the card is replaced, the probability of picking a heart the next time remains the same, $\frac{13}{52}$ or $\frac{1}{4}$.

The outcome of the two events can be calculated by multiplying the probabilities:

$$P(\text{heart,heart}) = \frac{1}{4} \times \frac{1}{4} = \frac{1}{16}$$

Dependent Events

Events are **dependent** if the outcome of one event affects the outcome of another.

If the card is not replaced, the probability of picking a heart the next time changes to $\frac{12}{51}$ or $\frac{4}{17}$.

The outcome of the two events can be calculated by multiplying the probabilities:

$$P(\text{heart,heart}) = \frac{1}{4} \times \frac{4}{17} = \frac{4}{68} \text{ or } \frac{1}{17}$$

Mutually Exclusive Events

Two outcomes are mutually exclusive if they cannot happen at the same time.

Mutually Exclusive

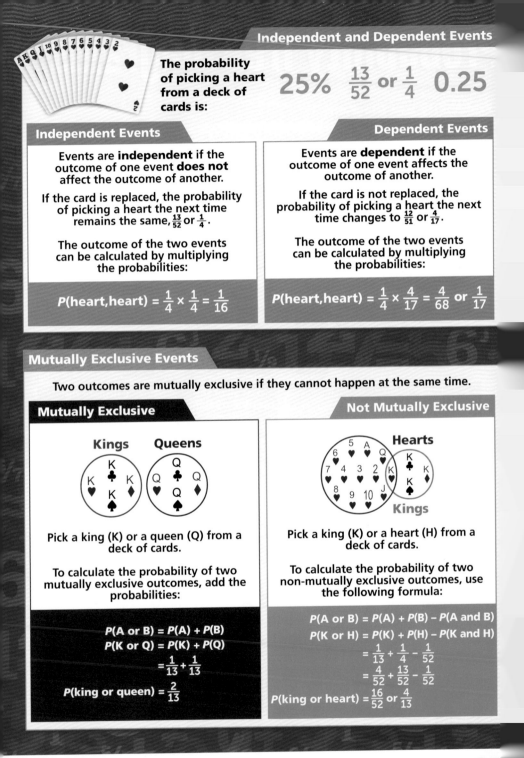

Kings   Queens

Pick a king (K) or a queen (Q) from a deck of cards.

To calculate the probability of two mutually exclusive outcomes, add the probabilities:

$$P(A \text{ or } B) = P(A) + P(B)$$
$$P(K \text{ or } Q) = P(K) + P(Q)$$
$$= \frac{1}{13} + \frac{1}{13}$$
$$P(\text{king or queen}) = \frac{2}{13}$$

Not Mutually Exclusive

Hearts

Kings

Pick a king (K) or a heart (H) from a deck of cards.

To calculate the probability of two non-mutually exclusive outcomes, use the following formula:

$$P(A \text{ or } B) = P(A) + P(B) - P(A \text{ and } B)$$
$$P(K \text{ or } H) = P(K) + P(H) - P(K \text{ and } H)$$
$$= \frac{1}{13} + \frac{1}{4} - \frac{1}{52}$$
$$= \frac{4}{52} + \frac{13}{52} - \frac{1}{52}$$
$$P(\text{king or heart}) = \frac{16}{52} \text{ or } \frac{4}{13}$$

Probability Tree Diagrams

Probability Tree Diagrams

Tree diagrams display all the possible outcomes of a series of events and help solve probability problems. Each branch in a tree diagram represents an outcome.

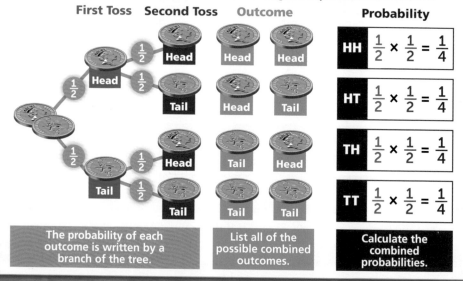

	First Toss	Second Toss	Outcome		Probability
				HH	$\frac{1}{2} \times \frac{1}{2} = \frac{1}{4}$
	Head	Head / Tail	Head Head / Head Tail	HT	$\frac{1}{2} \times \frac{1}{2} = \frac{1}{4}$
	Tail	Head / Tail	Tail Head / Tail Tail	TH	$\frac{1}{2} \times \frac{1}{2} = \frac{1}{4}$
				TT	$\frac{1}{2} \times \frac{1}{2} = \frac{1}{4}$

The probability of each outcome is written by a branch of the tree.

List all of the possible combined outcomes.

Calculate the combined probabilities.

Conditional Probability

The following tree diagram shows two dependent events, where the probability of the second event is dependent on the result of the first event.

Jane has a bag of 12 sweets: 7 red and 5 blue.

The probability of Jane picking two red sweets, if the first is not replaced, is $\frac{42}{132}$ or $\frac{7}{22}$.

$\frac{7}{12} \times \frac{6}{11} = \frac{42}{132}$ or $\frac{7}{22}$

$\frac{7}{12} \times \frac{5}{11} = \frac{35}{132}$

$\frac{5}{12} \times \frac{7}{11} = \frac{35}{132}$

$\frac{5}{12} \times \frac{4}{11} = \frac{20}{132}$ or $\frac{5}{33}$

To calculate the probability of a combination of outcomes, the probabilities of the outcomes need to be added together. For example, the probability of picking two different colours is:

$P(\text{red},\text{blue or blue},\text{red}) = P(\text{RB}) + P(\text{BR})$
$= \frac{35}{132} + \frac{35}{132}$
$= \frac{70}{132}$
$= \frac{35}{66}$

daydream
EDUCATION

Expected & Relative Frequency

Expected Frequency

The expected frequency of an outcome of an event, for a specific number of events, can be estimated using the following formula:

Expected frequency = Number of events × Probability of outcome

Ellie rolls a dice 12 times. What is the estimated frequency of her rolling a six?

Probability of rolling a six:

Fraction	Decimal	Percentage
$\frac{1}{6}$	$0.1\dot{6}$	$16.\dot{6}\%$

Expected frequency of rolling a six = $12 \times \frac{1}{6}$

$$= 2$$

If the results differ significantly from the expected frequency, it is likely that the event is not "fair". This makes the event biased.

For example, a dice can be weighted so that it lands on one number more than the others.

Relative Frequency

Probability is not always predetermined. For example, in football, a win, lose, and draw are not equally likely. In such situations, probability is estimated using relative frequency.

$$\text{Relative frequency} = \frac{\text{Frequency of outcome}}{\text{Total number of events}}$$

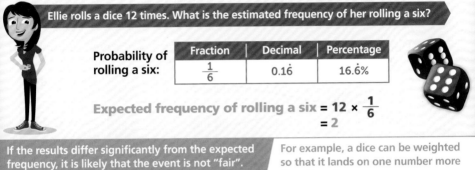

Daydream United's results and win probability were recorded at four stages during the season:

Results	7 games	14 games	21 games	28 games
Won	5	8	11	15
Drew	1	2	5	7
Lost	1	4	5	6
P (win)	$\frac{5}{7}$	$\frac{8}{14}$	$\frac{11}{21}$	$\frac{15}{28}$

$$\text{Win probability} = \frac{\text{Games won}}{\text{Total games}}$$

The most precise estimated win probability in the table is $\frac{15}{28}$ because it has been calculated from the largest data set.

In smaller data sets, the chance of anomalies is greater. For example, calculate the win ratio for the season (28 games) based on the win ratio from the team's first seven games.

Frequency Trees

Frequency trees are used to record, organise and present the frequencies of different events.

A group of students were asked if they thought they would go to university.

The frequency tree below shows that:

- **96** students were surveyed.
- **52** students thought they would go to university.
- **44** students thought they would not go to university.
- Of the **52** students who thought they would go to university, **40** did and **12** did not.
- Of the **44** students who thought they would not go to university, **21** did and **23** did not.

Thought they would go to university   **Ended up going to university**   **Relative Frequencies**

96

Yes → 52
No → 44

52 → Yes → 40
52 → No → 12
44 → Yes → 21
44 → No → 23

The leaves show the frequencies of each outcome.

The branches show the decisions or possible outcomes.

YY	$\frac{40}{96} = 0.42$
NN	
YN	$\frac{12}{96} = 0.13$
NY	$\frac{21}{96} = 0.22$
NN	$\frac{23}{96} = 0.24$

All rounded to 2 d.p.

Example Question

There are 32 pupils in class 2a, including 18 boys. 8 boys cannot swim. 10 girls can swim.

Create a frequency tree for this scenario, and calculate the probability of a pupil chosen at random being a girl who can swim.

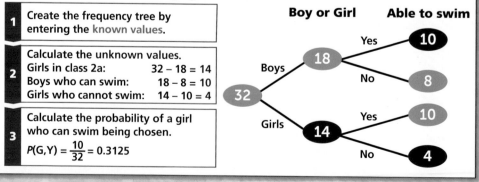

| 1 | Create the frequency tree by entering the known values. |

| 2 | Calculate the unknown values.
Girls in class 2a: $32 - 18 = 14$
Boys who can swim: $18 - 8 = 10$
Girls who cannot swim: $14 - 10 = 4$ |

| 3 | Calculate the probability of a girl who can swim being chosen.
$P(G,Y) = \frac{10}{32} = 0.3125$ |

Boy or Girl   **Able to swim**

32

Boys → 18
Girls → 14

18 → Yes → 10
18 → No → 8
14 → Yes → 10
14 → No → 4

daydream
EDUCATION

Venn Diagrams

A Venn diagram uses circles to illustrate the relationships between data sets or groups.

Sets are collections of related data or elements. The data can be text or numerical.

Sets are written within curly brackets:

Amphibians: {frogs, toads, newts, salamanders}

Prime numbers: {2, 3, 7, 11, 13, 17, 19, 23}

Notation

A Venn diagram begins with a box which represents the universal set – the set that contains everything. It is denoted by the symbol ξ. All other sets are subsets.

$A \cap B$: the intersection of A and B

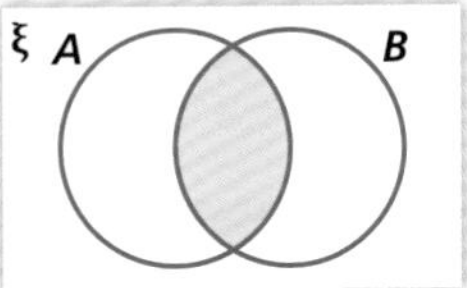

$A \cup B$: the union of A and B

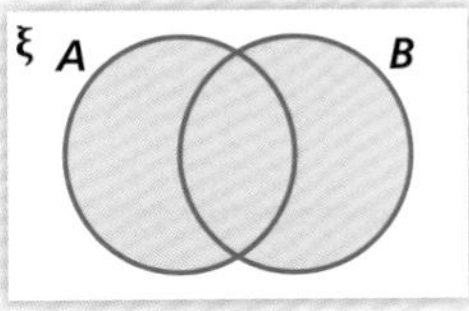

A': everything not in A

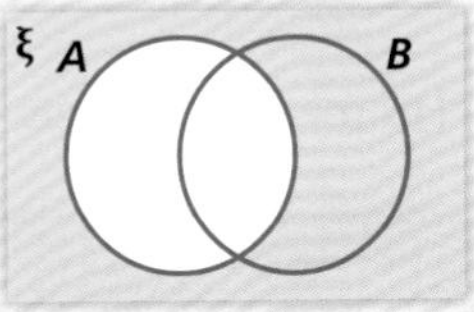

$A' \cap B$: everything not in A but in B

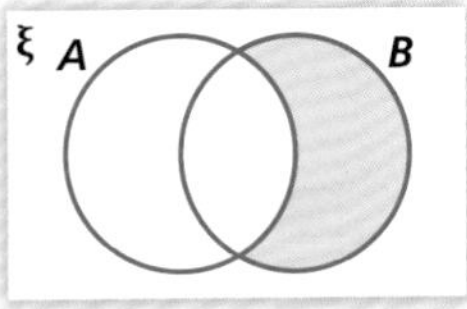

$A' \cup B$: the union of A' and B

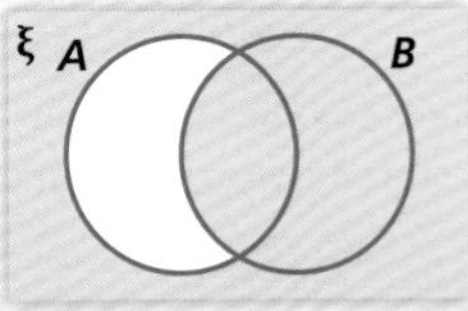

$(A \cup B)' = A' \cap B'$: everything not in the union

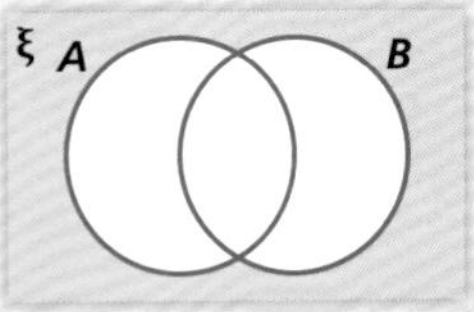

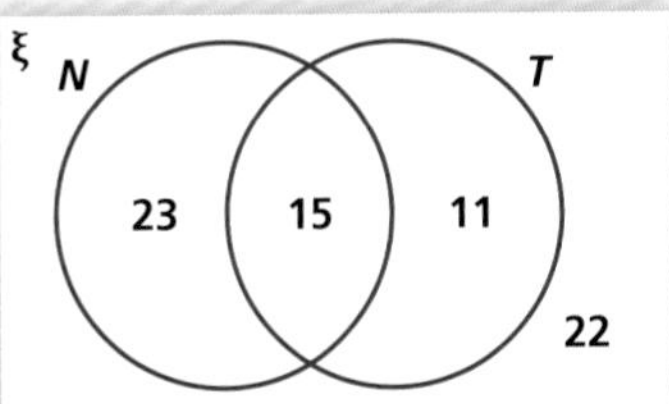

The Venn diagram shows that:

38 people play netball = N

26 people play tennis = T

23 people play just netball = $N \cap T'$

11 people play just tennis = $N' \cap T$

15 people play tennis and netball = $N \cap T$

22 people don't play tennis or netball = $(N \cup T)'$ or $N' \cap T'$

N = Play netball T = Play tennis

Finding Probabilities from Venn Diagrams

To find the probability that a random person in the sample group plays tennis and netball:

1 Calculate the total number of people.	**2** Identify the number of people who play tennis and netball.	**3** Calculate the probability using the probability formula.
$23 + 15 + 11 + 22 = 71$	15	$\frac{15}{71} = 0.21$ (2 d.p.)

The probability that a random person from the sample group plays tennis and netball is 0.21.

daydream EDUCATION

Averages

An average is a measure of the middle value of a data set. There are three main types of averages: mean, mode and median.

1 Mean

The mean is the sum of the values divided by the number of values.

$$\text{Mean} = \frac{\text{Sum of values}}{\text{Number of values}}$$

Joe was pleased with his exam results:

Geography	Biology	French	English	Maths	Music	Art
88%	72%	79%	77%	81%	68%	88%

His mean mark was $= \dfrac{88 + 72 + 79 + 77 + 81 + 68 + 88}{7} = \dfrac{553}{7} = \mathbf{79\%}$

2 Mode

Geography 88% Art 88%

The mode is the value that occurs most often.

The mode for Joe's results was 88%. It occurred twice, in Geography and Art.

3 Median

The median is the middle value when the data is arranged in order of size.

Music	Biology	English	French	Maths	Geography	Art
68%	72%	77%	79%	81%	88%	88%

The median for Joe's results is 79% because the French result is in the middle.
If there is an even number of values, then the median is the mean of the middle two values.

Range

The range is the difference between the lowest value and the highest value in a data set.

Music	Biology	English	French	Maths	Geography	Art
68%	72%	77%	79%	81%	88%	88%

Range = 20

To find the range, subtract the lowest value from the highest value. The range of Joe's results is 20.

Collecting Data

Primary data is obtained through first-hand investigation whereas secondary data has been collected by someone else.

Type of Data

Qualitative data is described using words: colour flavour sport

Quantitative data has a numerical value. E.g.: age distance weight

There are two types of quantitative data:

Discrete data includes only distinct values. For example, the number of people with blue eyes can only be a whole number.

Continuous data can take an infinite number of values (within a range). For example, a person's height could be any value between 0.5 m and 2.5 m on a number line.

Sampling

It is not always possible to collect information on a whole population. In such instances, a proportion (sample) of the population is used. Sampling methods include:

Random Sampling

The sample population is selected at random.

Systematic Sampling

A starting point is chosen, and a sample is then selected at regular intervals (e.g. every ten).

Start

Stratified Sampling

The population is split into evenly sized groups. A random sample is then taken from each group.

Bias

A sample that is not representative of a population is said to be biased.

It is not always easy to select a sample population that truly reflects the total population. When selecting a sample, consider the following:

Time and Date of Survey

Biased example:

A survey of what time people wake up conducted at 7 a.m.

07:00

This does not include people who wake up after 7 a.m.

Location of Survey

Biased example:

An Internet survey on the frequency of Internet use

This will not include people who do not use the Internet.

Demographics of Sample

Biased example:

A survey population of school children

This will reflect the views of only one age demographic.

The size of the sample also needs to reflect the survey population. For example, a sample size of 50 people will not accurately reflect the views of a whole country.

103

Frequency Tables

A frequency table is used to record how often a value (or set of values) occurs.

Frequency tables can be arranged in rows or columns. Sometimes the frequency is counted as a tally. These tables show the number of computers owned by students.

No. of computers	0	1	2	3	4
Frequency	0	5	8	7	2

No. of computers	Frequency
0	0
1	5
2	8
3	7
4	2

Averages from Frequency Tables

You can use frequency tables to calculate averages. Look at the table below. It shows the number of goals scored by players in a hockey tournament.

No. of goals (x)	Frequency (f)	Total no. of goals ($x \times f$)
0	6	0
1	10	10
2	14	28
3	10	30
4	8	32
5	2	10
Total	**50**	**110**

Range

The difference between the highest and lowest number of goals: 5 – 0 = 5

Mode

The category with the highest frequency (or most entries)

Mean

The totals from the frequency column and the total number of goals column can be used to calculate the mean:

$$\text{Mean} = \frac{\text{Total number of goals}}{\text{Total frequency (number of players that scored)}} = \frac{110}{50} = 2.2$$

Median

The position of the median can be determined using the formula $(n + 1) \div 2$, where n is the total frequency. Therefore, $(50 + 1) \div 2 = 25.5$.

The median number of goals is between the 25th and 26th values.

Now that you know the position of the median value, add the frequencies until you find which category the 25.5th value is in.

0 goals = 6 ✗   1 goal = 6 + 10 = 16 ✗   2 goals = 6 + 10 + 14 = 30 ✓

The 2-goal category contains the 17th–30th values, so the 25.5th value must be within this category. Therefore, the median is 2 goals.

daydream
EDUCATION

Grouped Frequency Tables

Grouped frequency tables organise data into intervals and are often used for large data sets. The table (on the right) shows the ages of people at a concert.

The age interval $15 \le a < 25$ is equal to or greater than 15 and less than 25.

Age (a)	Frequency (f)
$15 \le a < 25$	4,983
$25 \le a < 35$	5,679
$35 \le a < 45$	3,219
$45 \le a < 55$	1,823
$55 \le a < 65$	946
$65 \le a < 75$	210
Total	16,860

Averages from Grouped Frequency Tables

In grouped frequency tables, exact data values are not known. Therefore, averages can only be estimated. To do this, two extra columns need to be added to the table:

Also called the mid-interval value

Range

The difference between the lowest and highest ages:
$75 - 15 = 60$

Modal class

The category with the highest frequency

Age (a)	Frequency (f)	Midpoint (x)	$f \times x$
$15 \le a < 25$	4,983	20	99,660
$25 \le a < 35$	5,679	30	170,370
$35 \le a < 45$	3,219	40	128,760
$45 \le a < 55$	1,823	50	91,150
$55 \le a < 65$	946	60	56,760
$65 \le a < 75$	210	70	14,700
Total	16,860	–	561,400

Mean

The mean can be estimated using the totals from the frequency (f) and frequency × mid-interval ($f \times x$) columns.

$$\text{Mean} = \frac{\text{Total ages}}{\text{Total frequency (number of people at concert)}} = \frac{561,400}{16,860} = 33.3 \text{ (1 d.p.)}$$

Median

The class containing the median can be found using the following formula:

Position of median $= (n + 1) \div 2$

$(16,860 + 1) \div 2 = 8,430.5$

The median is the 8,430.5th value, which is in the $25 \le a < 35$ class.

Bar Charts, Pictograms & Histograms

Bar Charts

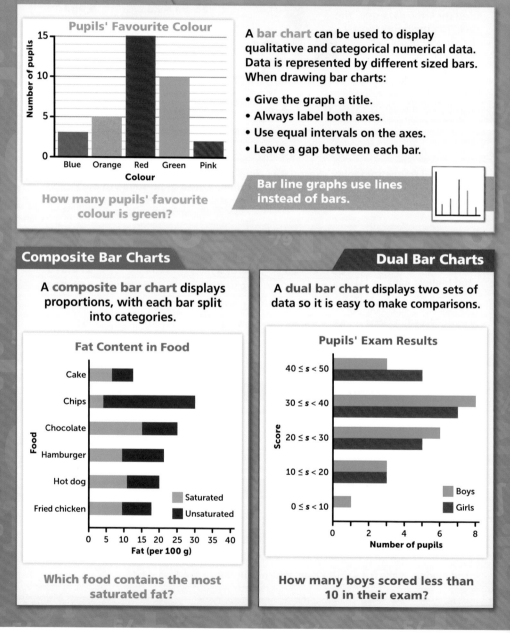

Pupils' Favourite Colour

A **bar chart** can be used to display qualitative and categorical numerical data. Data is represented by different sized bars. When drawing bar charts:

- Give the graph a title.
- Always label both axes.
- Use equal intervals on the axes.
- Leave a gap between each bar.

Bar line graphs use lines instead of bars.

How many pupils' favourite colour is green?

Composite Bar Charts

A **composite bar chart** displays proportions, with each bar split into categories.

Fat Content in Food

Which food contains the most saturated fat?

Dual Bar Charts

A **dual bar chart** displays two sets of data so it is easy to make comparisons.

Pupils' Exam Results

How many boys scored less than 10 in their exam?

daydream EDUCATION

Pictograms

Pupils' Favourite Ice Cream Flavour

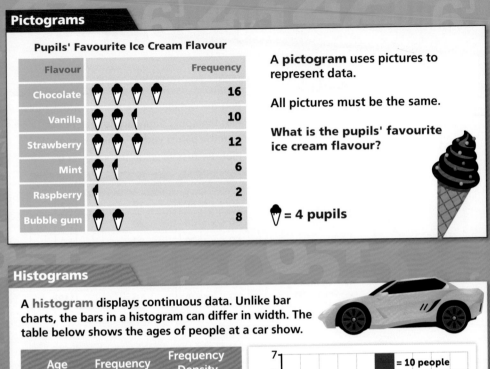

Flavour		Frequency
Chocolate	🍦🍦🍦🍦	16
Vanilla	🍦🍦🍦	10
Strawberry	🍦🍦🍦	12
Mint	🍦🍦	6
Raspberry	🍦	2
Bubble gum	🍦🍦	8

A **pictogram** uses pictures to represent data.

All pictures must be the same.

What is the pupils' favourite ice cream flavour?

🍦 = 4 pupils

Histograms

A **histogram** displays continuous data. Unlike bar charts, the bars in a histogram can differ in width. The table below shows the ages of people at a car show.

Age	Frequency	Frequency Density
$0 \leq a < 10$	0	—
$10 \leq a < 20$	10	$10 \div 10 = 1$
$20 \leq a < 30$	40	$40 \div 10 = 4$
$30 \leq a < 50$	100	$100 \div 20 = 5$
$50 \leq a < 60$	40	$40 \div 10 = 4$
$60 \leq a < 70$	35	$35 \div 10 = 3.5$
$70 \leq a < 90$	60	$60 \div 20 = 3$

■ = 10 people

The y-axis in a histogram is labelled 'Frequency density', not 'Frequency'.

The frequency density can be calculated based on data from the table:	Frequency density = Frequency ÷ Interval size = 60 ÷ 20 = 3

The frequency of an interval (area of bar) can be calculated based on the graph:	Frequency = Frequency density × Interval width = 4 × 10 = 40

Cumulative Frequency

Cumulative frequency tables keep a running total of the frequencies of a data set.

The figures from a cumulative frequency table can be used to draw a cumulative frequency graph. When plotting the points for a cumulative frequency chart:

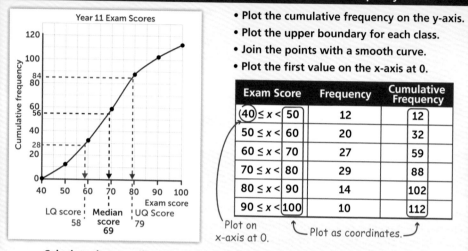

- Plot the cumulative frequency on the y-axis.
- Plot the upper boundary for each class.
- Join the points with a smooth curve.
- Plot the first value on the x-axis at 0.

Exam Score	Frequency	Cumulative Frequency
$40 \leq x < 50$	12	12
$50 \leq x < 60$	20	32
$60 \leq x < 70$	27	59
$70 \leq x < 80$	29	88
$80 \leq x < 90$	14	102
$90 \leq x < 100$	10	112

Plot on x-axis at 0.

Plot as coordinates.

Calculate the quartile and median positions, and then use the graph to find the lower quartile (LQ), upper quartile (UQ) and median scores.

LQ position $= \frac{1}{4} \times 112 = 28$

Median position $= \frac{1}{2} \times 112 = 56$

UQ position $= \frac{3}{4} \times 112 = 84$

Interquartile range $= 79 - 58 = 21$

Box Plots

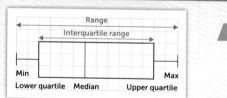

Box plots are used to display the spread of data.

They show the range, the interquartile range (the middle 50% of values) and the median. They do not show individual data values.

Box plots are used to compare data. The box plots below show waiting times at two hospitals.

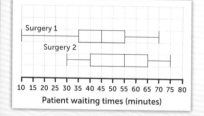

From the box plots, you can identify that:

The median waiting time at surgery 2 (55 min) is longer than at surgery 1 (45 min).

Surgery 1 (20 min) has a smaller interquartile range than surgery 2 (25 min).

Surgery 1 (60 min) has a larger range than surgery 2 (45 min).

daydream
EDUCATION

Pie Charts

A pie chart is a circular chart that is split into sections to show proportion. It is used to display categorical data.

Look at how the data from this frequency table has been displayed in a pie chart. The pie chart makes it easy to identify relative proportions of multiple classes of data.

Pupils' Summer Holiday Destination	Frequency
UK	21
Europe	34
America	5
Australia	1
Asia	3
Africa	6
Other	12
No holiday	14

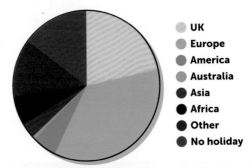

- UK
- Europe
- America
- Australia
- Asia
- Africa
- Other
- No holiday

The pie chart clearly illustrates that Europe was the most popular holiday destination.

The table below shows pupils' favourite sport. Follow the steps below to create a pie chart for this data.

Step 1: In a pie chart, data is represented as a proportion of 360, as there are 360° in a circle. Therefore, to calculate the proportion for each person surveyed, divide 360 by the total number of people surveyed: 360 ÷ 30 = 12.

Sport	Frequency	Frequency × 12	Proportion of 360
Rugby	4	4 × 12 = 48	48
Football	8	8 × 12 = 96	96
Cricket	4	4 × 12 = 48	48
Netball	6	6 × 12 = 72	72
Swimming	3	3 × 12 = 36	36
Tennis	2	2 × 12 = 24	24
Hockey	3	3 × 12 = 36	36
Total	30	30 × 12 = 360	360

Step 2: To calculate the proportions for each sport, multiply their frequencies by 12.
4 × 12 = 48

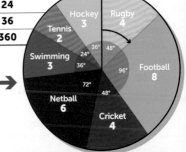

Step 3: Now that the sports have been converted to proportions of 360, the pie chart can be drawn.

Start by drawing a straight line from the centre of the circle to the edge.

Use a protractor to measure and mark the angles for each sport, and label them accordingly.

Car Sales

Time series graphs show patterns and trends in data over time. Data is plotted as a series of points that are joined with straight lines.

In this graph, a general pattern is repeated. When a pattern is repeated over a fixed and known period, this is called **seasonality**.

The graph also has an overall **upward trend**. This is shown by the red line.

Remember: Time is always plotted on the x-axis.

Moving Averages

Moving averages help identify general trends by 'smoothing out' seasonality. Over a period, if a pattern repeats itself every three points, take a moving average for every three points.

In the time series graph above, the pattern is repeated every four points so a four-point moving average is needed.

1 $\dfrac{180 + 550 + 430 + 532}{4} = 423$

2 $\dfrac{550 + 430 + 532 + 260}{4} = 443$

3 $\dfrac{430 + 532 + 260 + 576}{4} = 449.50$

Date	Sales (£000)
Jan-16	180
Apr-16	550
Jul-16	430
Oct-16	532
Jan-17	260
Apr-17	576
Jul-17	500
Oct-17	560
Jan-18	300
Apr-18	680
Jul-18	580
Oct-18	600

Car Sales

Plot the moving average points in the centre of each period. The points show an upward trend.

daydream EDUCATION

Scatter Graphs

Scatter graphs are used to show how closely two sets of data are related. Correlation describes how the two sets of data are related.

Positive Correlation

When the **plotted points** go upward from left to right, there is **positive correlation**.

As one quantity increases, the other increases. As one quantity decreases, the other decreases.

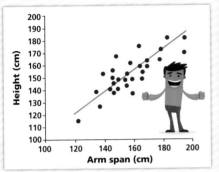

This graph shows that there is **positive correlation** between height and arm span. As height increases, so does arm span.

Negative Correlation

When the **plotted points** go downward from left to right, there is negative correlation.

As one quantity increases, the other decreases.

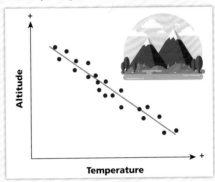

This graph shows that there is negative correlation between altitude and temperature. As altitude increases, temperature decreases.

No Correlation

When there is no linear relationship between two data sets, there is no correlation.

This graph shows that intelligence is not related to shoe size.

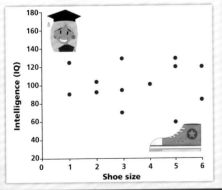

Line of Best Fit

A line of best fit is a line that is drawn through the centre of a group of data points.

When the plotted points are close to the line of best fit, there is **strong correlation**. When they are spread out on either side of the line of best fit, there is **moderate correlation**.

This graph shows a **strong positive correlation**.

Correlation and Causation

A correlation between two variables does not necessarily mean there is a direct cause-and-effect relationship between them.

Example >>> There is a strong positive correlation between number of cars owned and life expectancy. However, these variables are not directly related. Buying more than one car does not increase life expectancy. What other variable could be involved?

Mathematical Formulae

Area of a Rectangle — F

$$A = l \times w$$

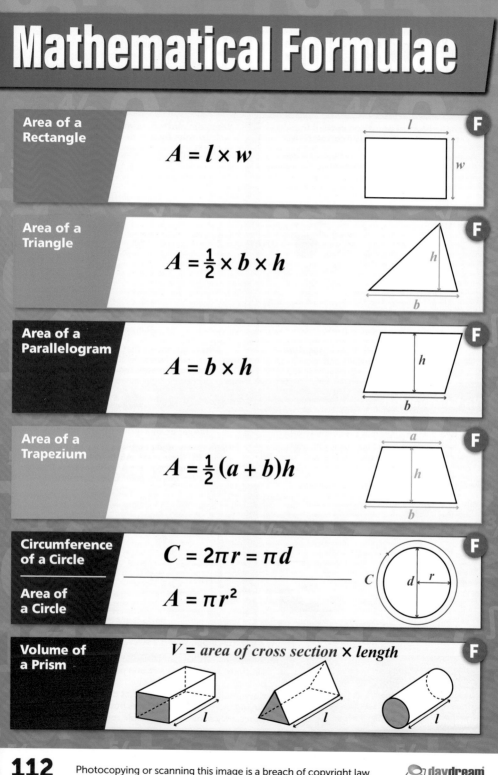

Area of a Triangle — F

$$A = \tfrac{1}{2} \times b \times h$$

Area of a Parallelogram — F

$$A = b \times h$$

Area of a Trapezium — F

$$A = \tfrac{1}{2}(a + b)h$$

Circumference of a Circle — F

$$C = 2\pi r = \pi d$$

Area of a Circle — F

$$A = \pi r^2$$

Volume of a Prism — F

$$V = \text{area of cross section} \times \text{length}$$

Pythagoras' Theorem

$$a^2 + b^2 = c^2$$

F

Trigonometry Formulae (right-angled triangles)

$$\operatorname{Sin}\theta = \frac{a}{c} \quad \operatorname{Cos}\theta = \frac{b}{c} \quad \operatorname{Tan}\theta = \frac{a}{b}$$

F

Trigonometry Formulae (any triangle)

H

Sine rule

$$\frac{a}{\sin A} = \frac{b}{\sin B} = \frac{c}{\sin C}$$

Cosine rule

$$a^2 = b^2 + c^2 - 2bc \cos A$$

Area

$$A = \tfrac{1}{2}ab \sin C$$

Compound Interest

F

$$Total\ accrued = P\left(1 + \tfrac{r}{100}\right)^n$$

Where P is the principal amount, r is the interest rate and n is number of times that the interest is compounded.

Probability

F

$$P(A\ or\ B) = P(A) + P(B) - P(A\ and\ B)$$
$$P(A\ or\ B) = P(A\ given\ B)P(B)$$

$P(A)$ is the probability of outcome A.
$P(B)$ is the probability of outcome B.

Quadratic Formula

H

The solution of $ax^2 + bx + c = 0$, where $a \neq 0$

$$x = \frac{-b \pm \sqrt{(b^2 - 4ac)}}{2a}$$

F Foundation **H** Higher

Notes